# A Primer of Statistics

# for Political Scientists

# A Primer of Statistics

# for Political Scientists

### V. O. KEY, JR.

**with a Foreword by Frank Munger**

## THOMAS Y. CROWELL COMPANY

NEW YORK · ESTABLISHED 1834

# FOREWORD

The far-reaching reputation of V. O. Key, Jr., in the field of political science has been closely associated with the use of quantitative techniques in the study of political behavior. Although Professor Key never claimed to be the first to apply quantitative techniques to politics—he was, if anything, overscrupulous in his acknowledgment of the work of his predecessors—a generation of younger American political scientists learned to respect the value of the quantitative method from the examples provided in Key's works on state politics and in his justly famed textbook on political parties and pressure groups.

In only one volume, however—*A Primer of Statistics for Political Scientists*—did V. O. Key consciously and formally set out to teach his readers the techniques of quantitative analysis. This book has been unavailable in recent years; its reissuance now, in response to repeated requests, is a distinct service to students of politics. Despite the decade and more that has passed since its original publication, it remains, in my judgment, the best work of its kind: an introduction to the use of descriptive statistics written for political scientists with minimal mathematical training.

The intervening years have brought changes, of course, but they are changes that make the book more vauable rather than less. When V. O. Key first wrote, skill in quantitative techniques was a rarity among trained political scientists. Increasingly it has become a competence expected even of undergraduate majors in the discipline. Undoubtedly, many teachers will wish to make use of the *Primer* in undergraduate courses in politics and political behavior. For graduate students in political science it is almost indispensable.

In still another respect times have changed. When Key first wrote, quantifiable data concerning politics was hard to come by; securing the information necessary for statistical analysis was a serious problem in itself. Today, thanks particularly to the work of such men as Walter Dean Burnham and Richard Scammon, and to the remarkable series of publications prepared by *The Congressional Quarterly,* a wide range of statistical series is available for research use even in quite limited libraries.

*A Primer of Statistics for Political Scientists* deserves and will receive a wide audience.

April 1966                                     FRANK MUNGER

# PREFACE

This is a preface that ought to be read. Otherwise the purposes, uses, and limits of the book may not be properly understood.

The objective of the chapters that follow is not pretentious. It is to introduce the student who is unaware of the difference between a square root and a standard deviation to the most elementary techniques of quantitative analysis. The aim has been to explain simply a few of the more common and more useful statistical procedures by illustrative applications to the data of politics in order that the book might be readily comprehensible to political scientists, historians, and others concerned with political studies. For the treatment of many questions of politics only the simplest quantitative techniques are either necessary or sensible. As a "how to" handbook for such analyses the book can stand on its own feet. The student who wishes really to dig into statistical technique on his own may find this volume, with its illustrative cases drawn from familiar material, useful as an aid in finding his way into more advanced treatments.

A general point of view of the book is that quantitative procedures may be best regarded as particular techniques by which more general methods of reasoning may be applied to the data of politics. Hence, the discussion may be suggestive to students concerned about systematic political analysis regardless of whether they need to learn the intricacies of quantitative technique. A virtue of the statistical approach is that it brings explicitly and nakedly to attention general questions of analytical method.

I can claim no standing in the statistical guild, yet my own work has persuaded me of the considerable utility of simple quantitative techniques, and a steady stream of bewildered students seeking guidance has convinced me of the need for a practical handbook geared to the needs of the student of politics who lacks training in statistics. Hence, I have ventured where a more prudent man would not have trod; I can only pray the understanding indulgence of my colleagues of the statistical faculties. Once an extensive body of statistical technique especially adapted to the problems and data of politics develops and becomes conventionally accepted, we may expect a comprehensive guide to be prepared by a person with credentials both as a statistician and as a student of politics.

A set of simple exercises has been included whose execution may aid the student to learn how to work with figures. The exercises have been formulated with an eye to relating the acquisition of technique to problems of interest to the student of politics. Other and more suitable exercises to relate technique to substantive questions of special concern to the individual student will doubtless occur to student and instructor. The more closely instruction in research method is geared to work on substantive matters, the more effective it is likely to be.

For so brief a book I must make a formidable number of acknowledgments. My principal debt is to my assistant, David M. Heer, who has labored with diligence to bring me to an understanding of some of the mysteries of statistics. He prepared drafts of most of the sections explanatory of the more technical statistical procedure. Yet he should not be held accountable for them in their present form, since I have done some violence to the technical niceties in my efforts to translate statistical language into the tongue the rest of us use. I have benefited from criticisms by my colleagues Louis Hartz, Duncan MacRae, Jr., and G. H. Orcutt. I am especially obliged to Professor David B. Truman, of Columbia University, for his helpful comments on the manuscript. Assistance in various ways in the making of the book came from

Jean Ackerman, Layman Allen, Margaret Churchill, Aniela Lich-
tenstein, Frank Munger, and Corinne Silverman. The undertaking
represents a by-product of an inquiry into electoral behavior sup-
ported by the Rockefeller Foundation, to which organization I am
deeply indebted for assistance on various occasions. All these acknowledgments do not dilute my responsibility for the errors of
commission and the sins of omission. If students who chance to
plow through these pages will call the boners to my attention, I
shall be grateful.

November, 1953                                    V. O. KEY, JR.

# CONTENTS

# A Primer of Statistics

# for Political Scientists

the *Financial Statistics of States.* Or, the statistics for her paper came from the *Social Security Bulletin.* Those versed in statistics only reluctantly reconcile themselves to such barbarous usages. They prefer to apply the term "data" or perhaps "observations" to such figures. They include within the term *statistics* methods for the collection, condensation, summarization, interpretation, and analysis of data in numerical form. Within this broad conception, however, two types of approach must be differentiated in our essay toward the simplification of statistical method.

One broad category of applications of statistical methods may be regarded as *descriptive* statistics. Given a formless mass of data or a jumble of apparently meaningless observations, one can, by relatively simple statistical operations, describe certain characteristics of the mass, measure the relations involved among its units, and put it into a form to facilitate its interpretation through conventional logical methods. Descriptive statistics is the chief concern of the following chapters.

By the application of the techniques of descriptive statistics we can state, with some precision, the characteristics of a particular *population,* e.g., all members of the House of Representatives of the Eighty-second Congress; all voters in the thirteenth precinct of the third ward; all cities of over 10,000 inhabitants in the United States. Such applications are regarded as elementary by those with statistical virtuosity. Scientific inquiries that rely heavily on statistics utilize the procedures of statistics not so much for description of total populations as for what is sometimes called *statistical inference.* Fundamentally, this phase of statistics seeks to describe *entire* populations by the inspection of relatively small *samples.* In statistical inference the techniques of descriptive statistics are employed to measure the characteristics of samples. Over these measurements are superimposed tests of significance to estimate the probability that the measurements of the sample indicate, within some specified range, the characteristics of the entire population. A typical question would be, What are the odds that the percentage division of a sample of voters polled falls within plus or minus two points of the division of the entire electorate? The intricacies of the procedures for dealing with such questions often cause the neophyte to abandon his forays into statistics in a state of confusion. Since the uses to which most political scientists can readily put statistical procedures are descriptive of total populations, emphasis may be placed on descriptive techniques. Reserved for the concluding chapter is a brief discussion of statistical inference and its relation to political inquiry.

This first chapter will set forth several quite simple descriptive procedures. Their simplicity may cause the student to wonder why they receive so extended an exposition. As will be seen in later chapters, however, more complex statistical operations are built in part on the simple procedures set forth in this chapter.

## 1. Arranging Frequency Distributions

Two terms with which the student of statistics soon becomes familiar are *frequency* and *variable*. Frequency is a term that defines itself, but variable requires a bit of explanation. In an abstract way it may be said that variables take the form of quantities that vary in value. One may have, for example, a list of 3,000 counties with the average monthly old-age assistance payment in each. The variable, the average monthly payment, is measured in quantities of dollars. In a list of 500 townships with the average per capita annual expenditure of each, the variable of expenditure again is measured in dollars. In a city with 750 voting precincts Republican strength could appear as a variable measured by the percentage of the vote Republican in each precinct.

Unorganized masses of data, such as that assembled for our lists of counties, townships, or precincts, have little or no meaning unless they can be transmuted into a compact form that conveys some notion of the nature and dimensions of the entire aggregate of data. That condensation may be accomplished by arranging the figures representing the variable in question into a *frequency distribution*. Such an arrangement indicates the frequency with which specified values occur through the *range* of the *series*. Assume that our old-age assistance payments varied from a low of $25.00 to a peak of $100.00. These two figures would be at the extremes of the range of our particular series, that is, all the measurements of the variable in question. The frequency distribution itself would show the number of counties that paid, say, from $25–$39, the number that paid from $40–$54, and so on through the series.

Frequency distributions may be presented as *frequency tables* or in a variety of graphic forms. A frequency table indicates, as the name implies, the number of times specified values or the number of times values within specified limits occur in the entire mass of data. By this means dozens, or thousands, of individual items can be reduced to a compact statement that constitutes a meaningful description of the whole. Although anyone can, and nearly everyone does, make use of frequency tables, a few rules of practice are worth knowing. Their violation, which is not uncommon, results in tables with ambiguously phrased captions, inappropriate groupings of items, imprecisely defined categories, and other inelegant features. In truth, the construction of a table that

TABLE 1

*Distribution of Cleveland Voting Precincts According to Total Vote Cast for Governor in Each, 1932*

| VOTES CAST | NUMBER OF PRECINCTS |
|:---:|:---:|
| 50–99 | 1 |
| 100–149 | 4 |
| 150–199 | 33 |
| 200–249 | 120 |
| 250–299 | 190 |
| 300–349 | 150 |
| 350–399 | 101 |
| 400–449 | 67 |
| 450–499 | 48 |
| 500–549 | 26 |
| 550–599 | 9 |
| 600–649 | 1 |
| Total | 750 |

Source: *Ohio Election Statistics, 1932*, pp. 218–42.

faithfully reflects the data and effectively conveys the intended message usually represents a far more trying task than the composition of the quantity of English prose necessary to fill an equivalent space.

A simple example will illustrate the main questions of form in building frequency tables. In 1932 the City of Cleveland had

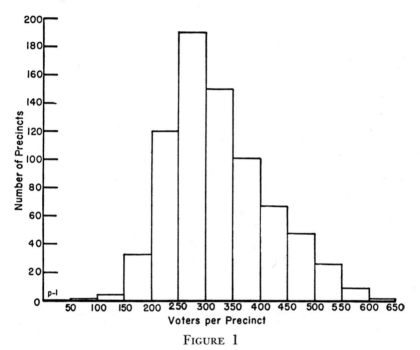

FIGURE 1

*Frequency Histogram of Data of Table 1*

750 voting precincts in which the number of votes cast in each ranged from 85 to 605. A list of precincts with the number of votes cast in each presents a confusing array of figures, but a frequency distribution gives a compact picture of the structure of precincts according to the number of votes cast in each. The data are so arranged in Table 1.

The basis for some of the rules governing the construction of tables can be better explained if the data of Table 1 are first put into graphic form. Two methods of representing the data are shown in Figures 1 and 2. The type of representation in Figure 1 is known as a *frequency histogram;* that in Figure 2, as a *frequency polygon.* The frequency histogram is simply a bar chart in which the vertical bars are proportional in length to the number

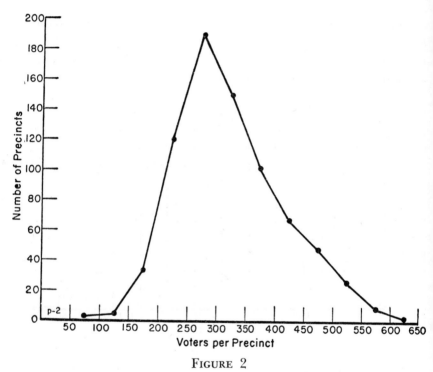

FIGURE 2

*Frequency Polygon of Data in Table 1*

of items in the classes of the frequency table which they represent. The vertical scale of the chart indicates the number of items in each class; the horizontal scale indicates the dividing lines between the classes. The frequency polygon, as may be seen from Figure 2, may be regarded simply as a variation on the frequency histogram. If one were dealing with extremely large numbers of instances in a distribution and grouped them into extremely narrow classes, the frequency histogram would approach in appearance a frequency polygon.

From either Figure 1 or Figure 2 certain characteristics of the distribution shown in Table 1 become obvious. An advantage of such graphic presentations is that they permit ready identification of these characteristics. As the extremes of the range of items are approached, the number of cases in each group declines, most of the items being clustered in the central categories. The distribution would be described as *skewed,* i.e., the largest category of items does not occur at the center of the distribution but falls, in this instance, to the left of the center. A skewed distribution, with its tail extending far to the left or right of the most frequent values, is contrasted with a distribution in which the largest category of items falls at the center and the smaller categories taper off symmetrically on each side of the center. A common type of *symmetrical* distribution, the normal, is illustrated by Figure 4 on page 10.

Many statistical problems revolve about the analysis of frequency distributions, but for the moment the relevance of Figures 1 and 2 rests in their bearing on the way one deals with the simple problem of constructing a table. Introductory statistics texts spell out at length rules-of-thumb to guide in the making of tables, but about all that the rules boil down to is the injunction that any table should reveal the form or shape of the underlying distribution of items.

In arranging items in a table one must determine the number of *classes* into which they are to be grouped and fix the width of the class *intervals.* The definition of the class interval, of course, fixes the number of classes. The most workable rule is that the size or width of the class should be small enough to assure that the tabulation reveals the shape of the distribution. Inspection of a mass of figures enables one to fix roughly the upper and lower limits of the data to be grouped. The range between upper and lower limits and the approximate number of cases provide a base by which one can, after a little experience, fix class intervals more or less by ear. It is prudent to tally the data by smaller class intervals than are likely to be used, so that classes of the tally sheet

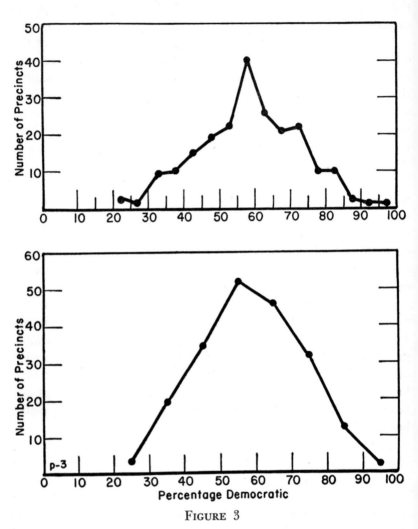

FIGURE 3

*Distribution of Sample Consisting of Every Other Pittsburgh Precinct According to Percentage of Presidential Vote Democratic in 1932, by Class Intervals of 5 Per Cent and 10 Per Cent*

may be combined by a certain amount of trial and error into the groupings most suitable for presentation.[1]

It is ordinarily considered good practice to make the class intervals large enough to assure a more or less smooth frequency polygon. Usually irregularities appear as the size of the class interval is reduced. In Figure 3, for example, two frequency tables of the Democratic percentage of the presidential vote in every other precinct in Pittsburgh in 1932 are presented as polygons. The polygon based on a frequency table with 5 per cent class intervals displays irregularities, whereas the polygon based on 10 per cent class intervals presents a more regular form. The statistician's desire to form a smooth curve comes from the assumption in dealing with samples that the true underlying distribution fits such a curve. If more and more instances were added to the sample, a regular curve would result. Hence, the curve based on a sample is smoothed to approximate the entire distribution. In descriptive statistics, however, arrangement of a table to bring out the irregularities in the distribution may be preferable in some instances because descriptions of some types of phenomena are inadequate if significant irregularities are not taken into account.

## 2. Measures of Central Tendency

When an array of instances is grouped in a frequency table, the mass of figures is put into a readily comprehensible form. From the table the range of the distribution may be seen, the point at which the largest number of instances clusters may be identified, and the general shape of the distribution discerned. Often for simple expository purposes a frequency table alone tells all about a distribution that needs to be told. For more exact analysis, however, measurements are available that describe particular

[1] In statistical work involving large numbers of items a good frequency tabulation saves a great deal of labor since certain characteristics of the distribution may be computed from the grouped data in the table rather than from the individual items. In making tables that are to serve as a basis for further computations one should be alert against a tendency of the cases to bunch at one or the other extremes of the class intervals. Computations from grouped data are made on the assumption that the mid-point of the class represents the value of the cases grouped together. Thus, error would be involved if all the cases in the class interval of 50–54.9 were bunched at 50.1.

characteristics of a distribution. One type of such measurement indicates the tendency of the cases to cluster around some central value within the distribution. Several *measures of central tendency*, as the statistical language goes, are available.

The more commonly used measures of central tendency are the *mean*, the *median*, and the *mode*. The arithmetic mean, usually called simply the mean, is the ordinary garden variety average. It is obtained by the division of the sum of the items of a series by the number of the items. The median is the value that divides

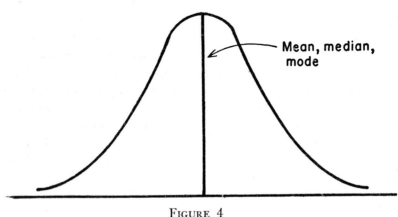

Mean, median, mode

FIGURE 4

*A Normal Distribution*

a distribution at midpoint, i.e., so that one half of the items fall on one side and the other half on the other of the median value. The mode is the value at which the items of a distribution are most heavily bunched; the mode may be estimated from a frequency table or a frequency polygon.

In a normal distribution the mean, median, and mode are identical. The symmetrical and bell-shaped distribution, illustrated in Figure 4, is called a *normal distribution,* and a goodly part of statistical inference turns around analysis of the normal distribution.[2] When a distribution is normal or even approxi-

[2] The curve representing a normal distribution is at times referred to as the Gaussian curve, after Gauss, one of its discoverers. The curve was found to fit the distribution of errors of observation in astronomy. Hence, it is sometimes called

mately so, one knows roughly something about the characteristic of the distribution from either the mean, the median, or the mode. Yet when distributions are markedly asymmetrical, the values of the measures of central tendency may differ radically and the determination of which measure to use becomes of some import.

In the choice of measures of central tendency, a basic question is whether a particular measure applied to a particular distribution will be meaningful when compared with the same measure applied to another distribution. All of which amounts to asking what the measure tells us about the distribution. In practice, the chief pitfall to which one should be alert arises in connection with markedly skewed distributions, for in such distributions the value of the mean diverges most from that of the median or mode.[3] When one measure of central tendency is used to compare two distributions, the conclusion from the comparison may be diametrically opposite from that flowing from the use of another measure of central tendency. That possibility is indicated by the distributions in Figure 5, which show the "party unity percentages" of Democratic and Republican Senators for the first session of the 82nd Congress.[4] The mean of the Democratic group is 77.7; that of the Republican, 77.8. This showing might lead to the inference that Republican party discipline was about the same as that of the Democratic party or at most a bit higher. When the medians are used as measures of central tendency, however, a

the normal curve of error. It also fits many distributions occurring in nature; thus, heights of 500 college students or their IQ's. A little knowledge of the normal curve may be a dangerous thing as when the marks of a class of fifty students are fitted to the curve. Yet the wide occurrence of natural distributions (and distributions of measurements) roughly in the form of the normal curve gives it an important place in statistics. Some types of political data roughly approximate the normal curve in their distribution and in such instances the curve is a useful model; it provides a base of expectation against which to observe actual behavior. Yet asymmetrical distributions seem to crop up in political data far more frequently than do symmetrical distributions. For a view that the normal distribution fits at least some types of political data closely enough to serve as a fruitful tool of analysis, see S. A. Rice, *Quantitative Methods in Politics* (Knopf, 1928), pp. 51–185.

[3] Measures of skewness, involving relations between the values of the mean and median, may be computed, but they are a statistical refinement scarcely necessary for the kinds of problems raised here.

[4] That is, percentage of votes with the majority of their own party on roll calls on which majorities of the parties were in opposition. *Congressional Quarterly Almanac*, vol. 7, p. 78.

different conclusion might be reached. One half of the Democratic Senators had a party unity percentage of over 83.5, whereas the median of the Republican Senators was 81.0. Although these differences are not great, they point to the importance of keeping

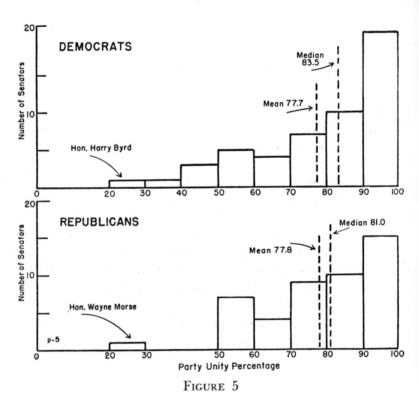

FIGURE 5

*Distribution of Democratic and Republican Senators According to Party Unity Percentage on Party Line Roll Calls, 82d Congress, 1st Session*

in mind that different measures of central tendency may yield different results in the comparison of distributions.

Figure 6 contains a pair of distributions that indicate the differences that may flow from the use of the mode and the mean in describing distributions. The mean score of Democratic Representatives in support of positions favored by Labor's League for Political Education was 7.9; that of Republican Representatives, 2.04 out of a possible 10. On the other hand, the modal Republican score was zero; the modal Democratic score, 10. The choice of indicators of central tendency depends on the feature of the distribution on which attention is to be focused.

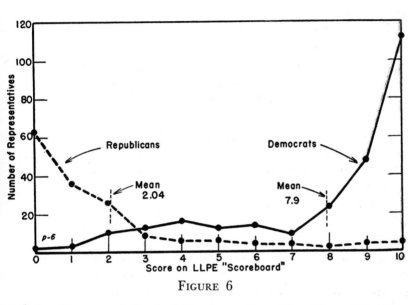

FIGURE 6

*What a Measure of Central Tendency Does Not Show: Distribution of Democratic and Republican Representatives According to Score in Support of Measures Favored by Labor's League for Political Education, 81st Congress, 1st Session*

There is no simple formula for the determination of which measure of central tendency to apply. The choice in particular cases should take into account the characteristics of the distribution on which emphasis must be placed to describe the significant aspects of the phenomenon under examination. About as good a rule as any is that in simple descriptive work one should consider using the median when the extreme cases or the skewness of the distribution pulls the mean markedly away from the midpoint of the distribution. The median at least tells the reader that half the cases in the frequency series fall on each side of it, no matter what the shape of the distribution may be.[5] The mean also has a uniform property from distribution to distribution, i.e., it falls at the center of gravity of the distribution, but that property is not often understood by non-statisticians. Of the mode, not much need be said. It is not a precise measure since a certain amount of discretion is involved in fixing its value. Its usefulness is limited to the most simple descriptive work. For example, of the distributions in Figure 5, it might be worth saying that the modal party-unity percentage fell in the range 90–100. The same figure illustrates the impreciseness of the mode. If a different class interval had been used, it could have been said that the modal percentage fell in the range of 90–94.9.[6]

Although an exercise of caution in the choice of measures of central tendency is wise, perhaps more important is a recognition of the extremely limited descriptive utility of any measure of central tendency, a word of warning justified by the manner in which averages are thrown around indiscriminately. It is most useful to keep in mind what measures of central tendency do not do in describing a distribution. Averages need to be supplemented by other descriptive measures, and quite often the more desirable choice is to present the entire distribution in either tabular or graphic form. Consider, for example, the two distributions whose frequency polygons appear in Figure 6. The basic data for the distributions consisted of a tabulation of voting records of Democratic and Republican Representatives issued by Labor's League for Political Education. For each of 10 major roll calls in the first session of the Eighty-first Congress, the League indicated whether the Representative had voted "Right" or "Wrong" from the League's point of view. From these data a score was constructed for each Representative ranging from 0 to 10, depending on the number of times he voted "Right" according to the League.

[5] For some types of data the median is the only usable measure. Thus, if one has a frequency table with an open-end category at one extreme, as "Incomes of $10,000 and over," the median may be estimated but not the mean.

[6] Those who pursue their inquiries further will encounter other measures of central tendency, such as the geometric mean, the harmonic mean, and the quadratic mean, all of which are more or less exotic measures that need not concern the beginning student.

The means of the Republican and Democratic distributions of scores, 2.04 and 7.9, convey an impression of a considerable difference between the two groups of Representatives, but note what the means do not tell us about the distributions as they appear in Figure 6. They convey no notion of the form of the distribution of either party group, whether symmetrical or asymmetrical. Knowledge of the form of the distributions in Figure 6—with the bulk of the Democrats located at one end of the scale and most of the Republicans at the other—would be helpful in comprehending the nature of the party groupings. Nor does the mean reveal anything about the *scatter* or *dispersion* of the individual values of the series about the mean. In one distribution the individual items may be widely dispersed around the mean. In another distribution with the same mean the items may be clustered quite closely around the mean; their scatter would be quite slight. Thus the mean score of the Democrats, 7.9, does not indicate whether all Democrats hover around that figure or are widely dispersed about it. When the shape of the distribution or its dispersion is important for the problem in hand, the measure of central tendency must be supplemented by measures of dispersion to bring out the characteristics regarded as significant.[7]

## 3. Measures of Dispersion

Although measures of central tendency have a usefulness in the description of distributions, they must often be supplemented by a measure of dispersion, i.e., a measure of the scatter of the items of the distribution around some measure of central tendency, usually the mean. The principal measures of dispersion are the *standard deviation* and the *average deviation*. The standard devia-

---

[7] The shape of the Democratic curve in Figure 6 has led this type of curve to be called a "J" curve. The Republican curve is sometimes called a "reverse J" curve. The data in Figure 6 incidentally may be described as "discrete" or "discontinuous"; all the items fall on the values of 0, 1, 2, 3, and so forth. The discontinuous features of the series would be more apparent if the score had been put on a scale of 0–100. The data in Figure 2, on the other hand, could be called "continuous" in that values of the variable may fall at any point. Incidentally, another way to present the data in Figure 6 so as to make the two polygons more comparable would be to convert the absolute figures of each class into percentages for each party group.

tion has usefulness as a measure of dispersion of a distribution, but an understanding of its nature is also essential because it is a component in a variety of other statistical procedures. The average deviation, a much simpler measure, has a considerably narrower range of utility. Its principal value rests in its simplicity and communicability to nontechnical audiences.

Since the average deviation is the simpler of the two measures, it may be described first, both to indicate its nature and to convey an understanding of the general problem of measurement of dispersion. The average deviation is the mean (or the average) of the deviations of the items of a distribution from its mean. An illustrative application, which also will indicate the method of computation, can be built on the following series of figures showing the population of Ohio congressional districts in 1950:

| DISTRICT | POPULATION (thousands) | DISTRICT | POPULATION (thousands) |
|---|---|---|---|
| 1 | 346.0 | 12 | 501.9 |
| 2 | 372.7 | 13 | 246.9 |
| 3 | 570.3 | 14 | 658.4 |
| 4 | 277.6 | 15 | 195.9 |
| 5 | 166.9 | 16 | 429.4 |
| 6 | 209.9 | 17 | 290.3 |
| 7 | 354.8 | 18 | 319.8 |
| 8 | 198.2 | 19 | 492.8 |
| 9 | 421.9 | 20 | 276.3 |
| 10 | 181.1 | 21 | 295.4 |
| 11 | 184.0 | 22 | 908.4 |

The mean population of the twenty-two districts was 359,000; obviously, however, the populations of the individual districts are scattered widely above and below this mean. The average deviation provides a measure of this dispersion. To compute the average deviation subtract the mean from each item of the series, ignoring signs. Or simply obtain the deviation of each item from the mean of the series. Then compute the mean of these deviations from the mean of the series. A simple procedure for carrying out this operation is to arrange the data from the table above as follows (with the items of the series, that is the district populations, in the column headed $X$ and the deviations of these items from the mean district population in the column headed $x$):

| DISTRICT | POPULATION $X$ | DEVIATION $x$ |
|----------|----------------|----------------|
| 1 | 346.0 | 13.0 |
| 2 | 372.7 | 13.7 |
| 3 | 570.3 | 211.3 |

The deviation $(x)$ for District 1 is obtained by subtracting 359.0, which is the mean of the series (conventionally represented by $\bar{X}$), from 346.0, the population of District 1 $(X)$, that is, 346.0 minus 359.0 equals 13.0 if signs are ignored. And so on through the entire series, which would produce a total for $x$, that is, for the deviations from the mean, of 2,966.7, which, divided by 22, the number of cases, yields the average deviation of 134.9, or 134,900.

The average deviation measures dispersion in absolute numbers. A particular average deviation has meaning only in relation to the mean from which it is calculated. In our example the average deviation of 134,900 has significance only in relation to the mean of 359,000 around which the instances were dispersed. Assume one series with a mean of 100 and an average deviation of 10 and another with a mean of 1000 and an average deviation of 10. Those average deviations, although equal absolute numbers, indicate the existence of dispersions sharply different in size in relation to their respective means. The first average deviation is 10 per cent of the mean, whereas the second is only 1 per cent of its mean. If one wishes to compare the dispersion or variability of one series with that of another, it is desirable to compute a measure of relative variability, that is, in this instance, a measure that relates the size of the average deviation to the value of the mean. In essence, what one does is to express the average deviation as a percentage of the mean of the distribution. The resulting ratio may be called the *coefficient of deviation*. In the case of the Ohio data the average deviation (134,900) divided by the mean (359,000) results in a coefficient of deviation of 37.6. (The coefficient is put on a scale of 0 to 100, as in the presentation of percentages, rather than on the scale of 0 to 1 that would follow from the use of the ratio produced by the division, 0.376.)

Since the coefficient of deviation is a measure of relative variation, it may be used to compare the degrees of dispersion of different distributions. Thus, if one were attempting to persuade an Ohio legislative committee that it had not approached as nearly as practicable the ideal of equality of population of congressional districts, he might search for comparative data. Illinois in 1950 had 26 congressional districts with a mean population of 334,000. The average deviation of these districts amounted to 36,800, but that absolute figure is not comparable with the Ohio deviation of 134,900 because the two deviations are measurements from slightly differing means—334,000 versus 359,000. However, the Illinois coefficient of deviation of 11.0 is comparable with the Ohio figure of 37.6. In effect, the average deviation of the Illinois districts was 11 per cent of their mean population; that of the Ohio districts, 37.6 per cent of their mean. With careful attention to presentation a coefficient of deviation could be gotten over even to a legislative committee. At least one could convey the idea to the Ohio solons that the state had a considerable way to go to approximate the degree to which Illinois had approached equality of district population.

Although the average deviation has its work-a-day applications, the *standard deviation* is far more widely used to measure dispersion. Its advantages, which will appear in due course, outweigh the greater difficulty involved in its computation. The standard deviation, usually represented by the Greek letter $\sigma$ (sigma), is the square root of the mean of the squares of the individual deviations from the mean of a series. (The deviation from the mean, it will be recalled, is the difference between the value of an item in the series and the mean of the series.) This definition may be clearer if it is presented in symbolic form, and this is as good a place as any to begin to become familiar with the more common statistical symbols:

Let     $\sigma$ equal the standard deviation;
        $X_1, X_2, X_3$—and so on through $X_N$—equal the values of the item in the series;

$\overline{X}$ equal the mean of the values of $X$;

$N$ equal the number of items in the series.

Then the above definition can be stated as follows:

$$\sigma = \sqrt{\frac{(X_1 - \overline{X})^2 + (X_2 - \overline{X})^2 \cdots + (X_N - \overline{X})^2}{N}}$$

This statement may be put more briefly if we use another symbol or so. If we let $x$ equal the deviation of an item from the mean, as was done in the explanation of the average deviation, and $\Sigma$ equal "the sum of," the above can be expressed as:

$$\sigma = \sqrt{\frac{\Sigma x^2}{N}}$$

The chief virtue of the standard deviation as a measure of dispersion is that a known proportion of the cases of a distribution

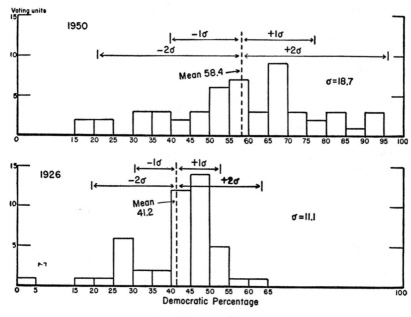

FIGURE 7

*Distribution of Detroit Wards and Other Wayne County Electoral Reporting Units According to Democratic Percentage of Two-Party Gubernatorial Vote, 1926 and 1950*

fall within one or more standard deviations from the mean, provided that the distribution is normal or approximately so. The properties of the standard deviation are illustrated by the distributions in Figure 7. One panel of the figure indicates the distribution, according to the Democratic percentage of the gubernatorial vote in 1926, of the wards of Detroit and the cities and townships of Wayne County used as electoral reporting units. The other panel in the figure shows the same data for the gubernatorial election of 1950. The figure also locates the mean and measures off one and two standard deviations from the mean for each distribution.

The properties of the standard deviation are such that, if the distribution is normal, 67 per cent of the cases fall within plus or minus one standard deviation from the mean and 95 per cent of the cases fall within plus or minus 1.96 standard deviations.[8] In any distribution, normal or otherwise, no less than 75 per cent of the cases fall between plus or minus 2 standard deviations from the mean and not less than 89 per cent of the cases fall between plus or minus three standard deviations from the mean.

The standard deviation of the 1950 distribution in Figure 7 is 18.7; that of the 1926 distribution, 11.1. If the 1950 distribution is described as having a mean of 58.4 and a standard deviation of 18.7, it is being said, in effect, that about two thirds of the cases fall within plus or minus 18.7 from the mean of 58.4. That is, such an interpretation would be correct on the assumption that the distribution is more or less normal. In fact, in this distribution 35 of 53, or 66 per cent, of the cases fell within the limits of plus or minus one standard deviation. On the other hand, the 1926 distribution is clearly irregular. An area of plus and minus one standard deviation from its mean encompasses 35 or 76 per cent of the 46 items of the distribution. Plus and minus two standard

[8] The proportion of cases falling within a range of plus or minus one standard deviation from the mean is obtained by calculating the proportion of the area under a normal curve that would be enclosed between lines drawn perpendicularly through the points indicating plus and minus one standard deviation from the mean. The same procedure would yield the proportion of cases expected to fall within any other multiple or fraction of the standard deviation from the mean.

deviations, however, includes 44 or 95.5 per cent of the items, more nearly what would be expected in a normal distribution.

Ordinarily a rough test of the normality of a distribution may be made by looking at its histogram. When one is working with small numbers it is also easy enough to determine whether the standard deviation behaves as it would with a normal distribution. Thus one may know whether to interpret the standard deviation under the assumptions applicable to normal curves or those applicable to any distribution. A simple graphic method of testing normality is by the use of arithmetic probability paper, sometimes called normal curve graph paper. The frequency table for the distribution is converted into a cumulative percentage table, that is, the percentage that the class of lowest values is of the total distribution is computed, then the percentage that the lowest class plus the next higher class is of the distribution is determined, and so on through the entire distribution. The data are plotted on the paper with the percentages on the vertical axis and the classes of the frequency table indicated on the horizontal axis. If a line connecting the plotted points is approximately straight, the distribution may be regarded as normal. The procedure is set out in detail in most elementary statistics texts.

Incidentally, comparison of the 1926 and 1950 distributions provides an illustration of the utility of measurements of distributions. Inspection of the two distributions suggests that a movement toward bi-polarization of the electorate, parallel with differentiations associated with residence, occurred during the interval between the two votes. In 1926 a few election units were Republican by 70 per cent or more, but by 1950 some lopsided majorities appeared also on the Democratic end of the scale. And from the histograms one sees that in 1950 the electoral reporting units were much more widely distributed over the scale of 1 to 100 than they were in 1926.

For the standard deviation, as for the average deviation, a measure of relative deviation may be calculated. This measure, the *coefficient of variation,* is the ratio of the standard deviation to the mean. In the example just given, a measure of relative deviation has disadvantages in that the standard deviation as computed is already on a scale of 100. The two standard deviations are in one sense already in comparable form. Thus, in 1926 about 95 per cent of the instances of the distribution were spread over a range of 44.4 points (i.e., plus or minus two standard deviations) on our scale of 100, whereas in 1950 it required 74.8 points on the scale to encompass 95 per cent of the cases. This limited sort of comparability is not, of course, equivalent to that which would be produced by the computation of a coefficient of variation.

To illustrate the coefficient of variation and its nature let us return to the absolute data in our case of the congressional districts of Ohio and Illinois. A literal execution of the formula for the standard deviation would involve a tabulation indicating the values of the series, the deviations with heed paid to the signs, and the squares of the deviations. The data on Ohio congressional districts would look like the following (with $X$ representing values of the items of the distribution, $x$ the deviation of a case from the mean of 359.0, and $x^2$ the square of the deviation):

| DISTRICT | $X$ POPULATION | $x$ DEVIATION | $x^2$ |
|---|---|---|---|
| 1 | 346.0 | −13.0 | 169.00 |
| 2 | 372.7 | 13.7 | 187.69 |
| 3 | 570.3 | 211.3 | 44,647.69 |
| 4 | 277.6 | −81.4 | 6,625.96 |

And so forth, through the entire series. The sum of the squares of the deviations, the column headed $x^2$, would be obtained. This sum would be divided by the number of cases, in this instance, 22. The square root of this mean is the standard deviation.[9] In practice, this literal execution of the formula need not be followed. A computational formula, outlined in the next chapter, produces the same result with less labor.[10]

---

[9] Another measure of dispersion is the variance, which is the square of the standard deviation or the mean of the squares of the deviations. The variance is widely used in advanced statistical procedures.

[10] Another labor-saving procedure is to compute the standard deviation from data grouped in a frequency table. The method is set forth in most elementary statistics texts.

For the Ohio congressional district data one obtains a standard deviation of 177,600 from a mean of 359,000. For the Illinois data the standard deviation is 49,600 from a mean of 334,000. The two standard deviations can be put into comparable form by the computation of the coefficient of variation, which is the ratio of the standard deviation to the mean of the distribution from which it was computed multiplied by 100 to put the coefficient on a scale of 0–100. Thus, for Ohio, $\frac{177,600}{359,000}$ times 100 equals 49.5. For the Illinois data, the coefficient of variation is 14.9.

In interpreting the coefficient of variation one has only to keep in mind the properties of the standard deviation. The coefficient of variation simply indicates that the proportion of items of a distribution within plus or minus one standard deviation from the mean falls within plus or minus the percentage that the standard deviation is of the mean. That percentage is the coefficient of variation. As has been seen, the proportion of items falling within plus or minus one standard deviation from the mean depends on whether the distribution is normal. If the distributions being compared are not assumed to be normal, a practical interpretation is that the items of the distribution with the larger coefficient of variation are more widely distributed relative to the mean than are the items of the distribution with a smaller coefficient, although the general rules given earlier about the meaning of the standard deviation as applied to any type of distribution may be used in interpreting the coefficient.

If normal distributions are being dealt with, about two thirds of the items fall within plus or minus one standard deviation from the mean of the distribution. Thus, if those conditions held, the Illinois coefficient, 14.9, would mean that approximately two thirds of the districts fell within plus or minus 14.9 per cent of the mean district population. In fact, 18 of 26, or about 69 per cent of the districts, fell within that range, approximately what would be expected for a normal distribution. On the other hand, the Ohio coefficient of 49.5 by its size alone arouses suspicion. So large a coefficient in relation to the mean suggests the existence either of an extremely wide dispersion of cases in relation to the mean

or of a markedly irregular distribution, with cases far from th
mean value at one or both extremes of the series. The irregularit
of the Ohio distribution may be confirmed by noting the siz
of the Ohio districts, especially numbers 12, 14, and 22. The effec
is that the range fixed by the coefficient of variation includes 7
per cent of the instances. The representative districts of Nort
Carolina provide an instance of a more nearly normal distribution
The standard deviation of the North Carolina districts, on th
basis as in all these cases of 1950 population before redistricting
was 46,500 with a mean population of 336,000. The coefficient o
variation of 13.8 fixed a range that included eight of the twelv
districts, or 66.6 per cent of the items in the distribution. I
dealing with distributions with small numbers of items one ma
anticipate minor departures from the proportions of cases ex
pected to fall within plus or minus one standard deviation. Ye
the moral of all this is that in the use of the coefficient of variatio
to compare the dispersion of different distributions tests should b
made for normality in the underlying distributions, or interpreta
tions should allow for the possibility of non-normality.[11]

## 4. Summary

Students are sometimes astonished when they collide with th
realization that many of the concepts of statistics are merel
mathematical synonyms for words of everyday discourse. Ordinar
conversation and writing are sprinkled with words and phrase
equivalent in intent with "mode," "mean," "average deviation,
"frequency distribution." The typical citizen of the Bronx vote

[11] For certain comparisons the standard deviation may be used without conver
sion to a coefficient. If one wishes to compare the position within distributions (
components of the distributions, the value of the component or of the mean of
sub-group may be described as plus or minus so many standard deviations from
the mean of the distribution. Thus, if one said that the mean party loyalty rat
of Democratic senators from Indianola was plus 1.1 standard deviations from th
mean of all Democratic senators, he would be saying that they outranked in th
respect something more than two thirds of all Democratic senators. One could com
pare this sub-group with other sub-groups in the same terms. If one thinks i
graphic terms, this process could be said to locate the central tendency of sub-grou
or a component of a distribution on a histogram, such as that in Table 7, in rela
tion to the entire distribution and its mean. For an illustrative application, see G. I
Grassmuck, *Sectional Biases in Congress on Foreign Policy* (Baltimore: Johns Hop
kins Press, 1951), chap. 7.

Democratic; most Vermonters are Republican; the average American abhors injustice; the usual situation is thus and so; the vote for the seven candidates was spread out; he generally wins in his home precinct by an overwhelming majority; and so forth.

All these and other such expressions have implicit in them a dim notion of at least some sort of impressionistic technique of observation as a basis for the conclusion that the particular characterization is applicable. The simple procedures described in this chapter amount to nothing more than systematic methods for handling masses of data or numerous observations in order that their characteristics may be described in terms that have a known and relatively stable meaning rather than the ambiguity of impressionism.

Although the description of frequency distributions, at least in so far as it has been presented here, seems a simple and commonplace matter, that process of description is a basic element in almost all kinds of observation and inquiry. The methods and concepts outlined here have relevance when one asks such questions as: What is typical? What occurs most frequently? Most infrequently? What is the relative frequency of any set of attributes? What is the range of variation of a series? And so on. The student of politics must cope with such questions even though he shuns statistical method. In practice such questions often have to be handled without benefit of statistical treatment. The theory of constitutional consensus rests, for example, fundamentally on assumptions about the distribution of attitudes and behaviors within the body of citizens, but the student of politics ordinarily does not possess the apparatus for the collection of data to test the theory. At another extreme questions of frequency distribution rise on questions affecting cases that are so few that statistical manipulation of the data would make no sense.

The simple concepts and examples of this chapter also make especially plain a proposition that will be repeated from time to time, viz., that statistical procedures will not do one's thinking for him. When one has processed his data in accord with one of the procedures outlined, he still needs to reflect about the meaning of his results. He should, of course, have had in mind some

broad question on which the computations would throw ligh
before he started the operation. Moreover, one must always see
to know his data. Thus, the distribution of Cleveland precinct
in Table 1 provides no safe basis for conclusions about the prope
size of precincts. Special circumstances may have prevailed to
justify the small size of some of them. Yet the distribution would
serve to guide further inquiry both to gain understanding o
the factors associated with the distribution and to guide in for
mulating recommendation. In political science, statistical proc
essing of data nearly always needs to be woven together in the
closest way with qualitative observations made in whatever wa
is appropriate in the particular case.

Another proposition that will bear both emphasis and repetitior
is that the choice of technique should be made in the light of the
nature of the problem being attacked as well as of the characte
of the audience being addressed. Some students seem disposed
once they learn how to compute a standard deviation, for example
to rush madly about computing standard deviations whateve
the problem and whatever the audience. Once a student compre
hends the broad notions of frequency distributions, measures o
central tendency, and measures of dispersion, he must use dis
crimination in the choice of techniques to cope with particula
problems. Thus, in this chapter several examples have been used
to illustrate the nature of the standard deviation. That measure
would almost certainly not be used if one were preparing a repor
as a staff member of a legislative reference service. The broad
concept of dispersion would be useful for analysis, but finding
would have to be put in comprehensible form. A variety of simpl
and understandable comparisons of distributions could be con
trived. For example, a finding that in State A 25 per cent of the
districts had populations in excess of 110 per cent of the average
population while in State B only 2 per cent of the districts di
verged so markedly from the average would be a comprehensibl
comparison of characteristics of distributions. On the other hand
a more precise analysis directed to a technical audience may re
quire the use of more conventional statistical techniques.

## References

### Method

F. E. Croxton and D. J. Cowden, *Applied General Statistics* (Prentice-Hall, 1939), chaps., 3, 8, 9, 10, 11. Readers will probably find their needs in an introductory survey of statistics best met by Croxton and Cowden.

F. C. Mills, *Statistical Methods Applied to Economics and Business* (Holt, rev. ed., 1938), chaps. 3, 4, 5. An excellent but less comprehensive treatment than the volume by Croxton and Cowden.

M. J. Moroney, *Facts from Figures* (Harmondsworth: Penguin Books, 1951), chaps. 4, 5, 6. Designed as a "layman's introduction to statistics," this Pelican Book has the advantage of low cost as well as lucid presentation.

G. W. Snedecor, *Statistical Methods Applied to Experiments in Agriculture and Biology* (Ames: Iowa State College Press, 4th ed., 1946). Distinguished by especially lucid and exact statements of methods of analysis and of the limitations of findings. The author believes that "statistical method can be used competently by scientists not especially trained in mathematics" and his book is written to make that possible.

L. D. Upson, *Letters on Public Administration* (Detroit: National Training School for Public Service, 1945), pp. 39–91. Sensible and practical remarks about fundamentals of research method and of statistical procedures.

A. E. Waugh, *Elements of Statistical Method* (McGraw-Hill, 3rd ed., 1952), chaps. 3, 4, 5, 6. An exposition of commendable simplicity somewhat more elementary and less comprehensive than the Croxton and Cowden volume.

### Applications

C. S. Hyneman, "Tenure and Turnover of the Indiana General Assembly," *American Political Science Review,* 23 (1938), 51–67, 311–331.

A. L. Lowell, "The Influence of Party upon Legislation in England and America," *Annual Report of the American Historical Association* (1901), I, 321–542.

S. A. Rice, *Quantitative Methods in Politics* (Knopf, 1928), chaps. 6, 8.

Julius Turner, *Party and Constituency: Pressures on Congress* (Baltimore: Johns Hopkins Press, 1951).

# 2

VVVVVVVV

# SIMPLE TIME SERIES

In ordinary language the term *series* implies a sequence through time. In statistical usage the word has several connotations. The preceding chapter focused on simple methods for analyzing and presenting *frequency* series, that is, series consisting of instances, cases, or observations occurring at a single point in time. The data underlying *time* series differ in that they consist of observations of the same or related phenomena at intervals through time. Some of the same techniques of analyzing frequency series or distributions may also be applied to the analysis of time series. Yet the time dimension constitutes an element of special importance in political analysis and calls for special methods of presentation and interpretation.

Simple time series have wide utility in the description and analysis of political phenomena. Events of political significance possess a time dimension of varying length. Patterns of partisan division of the electorate, for example, change through time. One form of municipal government may be substituted for another by degrees over a period of decades. At the extreme of brevity a pair of measurements of the attitudes of an audience before and after hearing a campaign speaker would also constitute a time series of sorts, although more commonly the term is reserved for data spread over longer time spans.

Here it is proposed to set out the most elementary rules and practices in the presentation of time series, with illustrative applications bearing on political behavior. In addition, some of the tricks in the derivation of meaning from series beyond the obvious descriptive facts will be suggested. These simple procedures warrant, because of their simplicity, a prefatory homily. The most complex methods of analysis and presentation are not always the most sensible. The conversion of a series of figures into a single graph on a chart often results in a more meaningful picture of the data than could be produced by the most elaborate statistical processing. And it is particularly fruitless to subject data that are in themselves crude in nature—such as most of the data of politics—to refined mathematical manipulations.

## 1. Graphic Presentation of Simple Descriptive Series

As an aid both to analysis and to presentation the conversion of a series of figures to graphic form is helpful. If the figures are transferred to a graph, the trend, if any, in the data becomes readily apparent. Regularities in fluctuation, if any, stand out. A graph brings sharply to attention the significant features of the series.

The student may test these propositions for himself by inspection of the following series showing the percentage of the estimated number of citizens of Ohio 21 years and over voting in the state's gubernatorial elections, 1920–1950.

| YEAR | PER CENT | YEAR | PER CENT |
|------|----------|------|----------|
| 1920 | 62.0 | 1936 | 70.5 |
| 1922 | 48.4 | 1938 | 56.1 |
| 1924 | 56.5 | 1940 | 74.6 |
| 1926 | 38.6 | 1942 | 39.4 |
| 1928 | 65.9 | 1944 | 65.6 |
| 1930 | 50.4 | 1946 | 47.3 |
| 1932 | 64.4 | 1948 | 60.1 |
| 1934 | 53.5 | 1950 | 55.8 |

Although the nature of the foregoing series is such that some of its significant features are obvious on inspection, compare the impression received from examination of the figures with that conveyed by the graph in Figure 8.

Certain conventions exist on the form of charts, whatever type of graphic representation is involved. Among the more important rules is that the caption indicate concisely and precisely the content of the chart. Readers are needlessly exasperated by captions that fall short of that objective. Latter-day practice seems to encourage also an interpretative tag-line on the caption to call at-

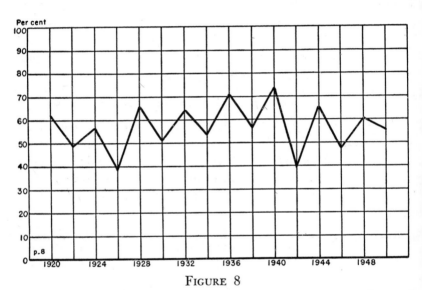

FIGURE 8

*Percentage of Estimated Number of Citizens 21 Years of Age and Over Voting for Governor in Ohio General Elections, 1920–1950*

tention to the feature of the figure to be emphasized. The urge to write a snappy title should not be allowed to defeat the end of precision. A title combining an interpretative tag-line with complete description appears on Figure 9, which may be compared with the more conventional title of Figure 8. The choice of form depends on the audience addressed as well as on personal predilection.

Other matters of form on which the meticulous place emphasis include a clear indication of the time intervals at the base of the

than are necessary. For some purposes coordinate lines may be reduced to stubs, as in Figure 9. Another general rule is that the sources of data on which a chart is based should be indicated by a source note below the drawing. As with most rules this one may be applied with moderation and discretion. Thus, most of the charts in this book have no source line since they are based on standard sources that are presumed to be familiar to the audience for which the treatment is designed.

Although the preparation of charts is not a higher form of art, the application of a modicum of skill and of ingenuity produces an attractive chart designed to draw attention to the characteristics of the series regarded as significant. By the manipulation of the ratio between the vertical and horizontal scales of a chart different types of impressions may be conveyed. Quite erroneous or distorted notions may, in fact, be suggested. Although manuals on graphic presentation suggest more or less fixed ratios between vertical and horizontal dimensions of charts, perhaps the best rule is that the person who prepares a chart ought to be aware of what he is doing. It is often legitimate to fix the scale of a graph so as to highlight a characteristic on which it is desired to focus attention. The same procedure may be employed to mislead the reader. The possibilities are suggested by Figure 9, which contains the same data as Figure 8. The enlarged vertical scale, the omitted zero line, the severed top of the chart convey, without careful inspection, an impression of fluctuation of far greater amplitude in turnout than does Figure 8. Space limits often make it necessary to telescope charts; when a section is sliced out of a chart for this reason that fact should be indicated by a break in the vertical scale, by a wavy line, or other appropriate sign.[1]

Save with respect to the most obvious and simple graphs, the analyst should spell out in the textual discussion his analysis of the data in the chart. Some readers do not have an eye for graphic representation. Even if they do, there is no certainty that they will read the graph in the same way as the author. The argument

[1] For other tips, see Darrell Huff, "How to Lie with Statistics," *Harper's Magazine*, August, 1950. The most appropriate response to the old saw about the veracity of statisticians is that it is much easier to identify liars who use figures than it is to spot those who rely solely on verbalisms.

has to be put twice: once in the text and again in the chart. In fact, many charts have served their purposes once the descriptive text is written; the text whose content is suggested by a chart can often stand alone.[2]

## 2. Interpretation of Single Time Series

Although the principal use of a single time series rests simply on its value as a description of the phenomena it records, certain types of interpretations can be derived from it. If the logical operation followed in this process is brought out into the open, some of the hazards involved can be avoided.

Inferences from single series usually involve some sort of "before" and "after" reasoning that relates shifts in the curve or graph to particular events. Moreover, this "before" and "after" reasoning takes place often without any "control"; that is, the interpreter does not have as a check—either on paper or in the back of his mind—a parallel situation in which the assumed cause of a squiggle in the graph did not exist. This reference to a "control" is somewhat cryptic; the general idea, which is fundamental to scientific inquiry, will be developed in succeeding chapters. It is in essence the question, "How do you know that the patient would not have recovered even had the doctor not been called?" Time series are often interpreted without explicitly testing by examination of a "control" situation the question

---

[2] So often are articles in the learned journals illustrated by abominable charts that it is worth mentioning that virtually no skill is necessary to prepare charts more or less professional in appearance. The really essential equipment consists of a ruling pen and a straight edge. Graphs can be readily drawn on cross-section paper and traced onto a transparent drawing paper in India ink. Lettering presents something of a difficulty. Unless a person is blessed with the knack of lettering, he should use a lettering guide, such as the Leroy lettering guide, a product of Keuffel and Esser Company, Adams and Third Streets, Hoboken, New Jersey, from whom a descriptive booklet may be obtained on request. The charts in this book were lettered by an amateur draftsman using such a guide. Another useful aid for the amateur draftsman is Zip-A-Tone, which is a trade name for transparent sheets on which cross-hatchings are imprinted in a variety of patterns. This material is indispensable for shading or cross-hatching areas on maps or for use on bar charts or any other type of chart on which it is desired to differentiate areas on the drawing. Zip-A-Tone can be readily affixed to areas on the drawing to be shaded or cross-hatched. The manufacturers, Para-Tone Company, 547 S. Clark St., Chicago 5, Illinois, distribute a chart showing the patterns available and including instructions for use.

whether the shift supposedly explained would not have happened in the absence of the offered explanation. Nevertheless, by main strength and some artistry and care in interpretation the bearing of non-quantifiable data, e.g., particular events or series of incidents, on the variations in a single time series may be characterized with some assurance. Quite apart from providing a means for such speculations about the effects of particular events, a graphed series often forms the basis for meaningful, qualitative description. Qualities of stability and of instability, of erraticism, and of uniformity of behavior may be readily identified.

## Uniformities in Time Series

The squeezing of meaning from single time series may at times be facilitated by an attempt to discern the "true" pattern of movement that underlies the imperfect regularities of a series. Secular trends, periodicity in fluctuation, and other uniformities appear clearly from inspection, although the graph always exhibits at least minor departures from its manifest general pattern. Various techniques are available to "smooth" curves and to fit regularly proportioned curves to the imperfect graph reflecting the data. The basic assumption in such an operation is that some underlying pattern or uniformity prevails in the phenomenon under examination but that random or non-recurring factors from time to time push the graph from its patterned course.

In economic analysis extensive use is made of techniques for fitting curves and lines to time series. For example, the secular or long-term growth in the number of business enterprises in the United States can be described by an ascending straight line. The graph of the actual series on the number of business enterprises fluctuates slightly below and above this straight line in reflection of the superimposition of the effects of booms and depressions on the underlying long-term growth trend.

The data of politics scarcely justify much use of refined methods to fit lines and curves to time series, but the basic ideas of the process have utility.[3] The conception of secular trend, a positive

[3] See, however, the examples of curve-fitting by Stuart A. Rice, *Quantitative Methods in Politics*, pp. 294–302.

or negative change over a long period of time, recurs in historical and political analysis. Often the trends dealt with consist of grand complexes of events not susceptible of measurement. At a more earthy level, however, it may be desirable, for example, to define and to describe the long-term trend, if any, in the partisan preference of a county or city. These purposes may be served by graph-

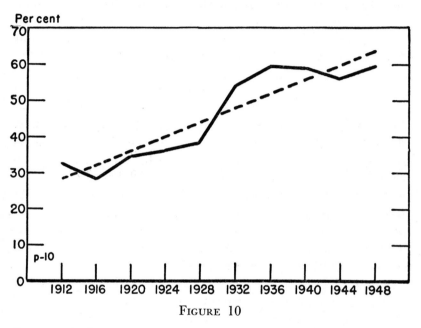

FIGURE 10

*Democratic Percentage of Total Presidential Vote, Perry County, Kentucky, 1912–1948*

ing the time series. It may even be useful to fit a line to the series by the method of least squares.[4] By that method a line is drawn that best "fits" the series in that the sum of the squares of the deviations of the actual points of the series from the line so located is at a minimum. The actual values of the series would not cluster so closely about any other line. A line so fitted is known as a line of regression.

[4] The explanation of the method of least squares is postponed for pedagogical reasons to a later point, pp. 78–81, 85–88.

The broken line in Figure 10, which was located by the method of least squares, is the line most nearly approximating the trend in the Democratic percentage of the total presidential vote in Perry County, Kentucky, 1912–1948. Although a straight line does not fit the data closely, the general picture suggests that perhaps this southeastern Kentucky coal-mining county, which had been traditionally Republican, slowly shifted its partisan allegiance as the rationale of its habitual party attachment became dubious. The county's apparent underlying general trend even offset the general dip in Democratic strength in 1928. Then the depression boosted the Democratic trend and the county departed from its Republicanism. All of which suggests that under conditions of incompatibility of traditional party attachment and current aspirations, traditional loyalties gradually wear away. The fitting of a line in itself, of course, proves nothing; the process represents only an attempt to descry the basic trend that is obscured by short-term oscillations. Perhaps an S-shaped curve moving from a plateau of low Democratic strength to one of high Democratic strength would better fit the data. The point is that the very process of fitting a line raises the question about the form of the underlying phenomenon and thereby sets off more or less fruitful inquiry or speculation.[5]

Another pattern that occurs in many time series is a cyclical or periodic fluctuation. An example appears in Figure 11, which shows the Democratic proportion of the two-party presidential vote in Oregon, 1896–1948. The identification of this type of pattern has led to considerable theorizing about cyclical behavior in politics, notably by Louis Bean. Earlier other political speculators, without benefit of such data, suggested the existence of a law of the pendulum in politics. The fact that extremely short time spans are covered by such series as that in Figure 11 makes it most hazardous to develop a general cyclical theory. The ups and downs of the curve may simply mirror a sequence of unique incidents rather than some inner nature of the political process that pushes toward a cyclical pattern of behavior.

[5] The case is taken from an extensive analysis of trends in Kentucky voting by John Fenton.

The student of politics needs to be sensitive to the possibility that many general propositions may be quite true but are not reflected in the available quantitative data. Thus, if the graph of presidential voting is pushed back earlier than in Figure 11, the cyclical pattern becomes dim and there is, of course, no warrant for projecting the line into the future. Yet the "law of the pendulum," in terms perhaps of policies and personalities, may

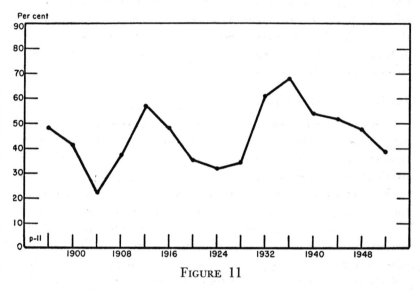

FIGURE 11

*Political Cycles: Democratic Percentage of Two-Party Presidential Vote, Oregon, 1896–1952*

be operative without necessarily reflecting itself in a cyclical pattern in the division of the presidential vote. An incidental yield from work with quantitative data consists of the hunches it suggests about the nature of phenomena for which no quantitative measure is available.

Periodicity of economic behavior, often in relation to the cycles of nature, results in extensive reliance on cycle analysis by economists. Some government administrative operations for the same reasons manifest a seasonality or a cyclical quality. Electoral behavior may have some cyclical characteristics associated with business cycles. There are, however, certain artificial periodicities introduced into political behavior by the regularities of the election calendar. In some instances these uniformities in a time series can be "correlated," so to speak, with non-quantifiable events. Thus, in Figure 8 (page 30) the rate of electoral turnout in Ohio clearly fluctuates in a two-year cycle, with the peaks occurring in presidential years. The obvious inference is that the greater interest in national issues and candidates, the more intense effort by party organizations, and the other factors associated with the presidential campaign and not with the campaigns of the gubernatorial year combine to produce the increased electoral turnout in presidential years.

## Deviations from Uniformities

Sharp deviations from generally uniform patterns in time series often provide evidence about the nature or significance of particular events that otherwise can be estimated only by the most undisciplined surmise. In the association of a particular incident with a departure from uniformity the assumption is made that the "normal" elements fixing the shape of the graph have a more or less uniform value throughout the time span and that particular events or incidents throw the curve out of its normal path at a particular moment. Thus, the graph in Figure 8 (page 30) showing the rates of electoral participation in Ohio gubernatorial elections indicates that the mid-term slump in turnout in 1950 was not nearly so great as in preceding mid-term elections. What, if anything, occurred in 1950 to maintain the relatively higher level of interest? In that year Senator Robert A. Taft fought a vigorous campaign against the Democratic candidate, Joe Ferguson, who was backed by labor groups hopeful of unseating the co-author of the Taft-Hartley Act. The relatively small drop in turnout gives plausibility to the inference that the 1950 senatorial campaign (as well perhaps as the concurrent gubernatorial campaign) had a vote-pulling intensity unusual for a mid-term campaign. (It is well to note, too, that the appearance of deviations from the uniformities of a series also is a signal for checking the accuracy of computations. Quite often a profound inference suggested by a deviation withers away with the correction of an arithmetical error.)

Hypothesizing the relation of particular events to deviations in series is often a bit treacherous because of the absence of a control. At times one can obtain something of a check on the validity of a particular interpretation. Reference again to Figure 8 (page 30) or to 9 (page 31) discloses that in 1934 the midterm slump in turnout in Ohio was far less than "normal." One might seek an explanation in some characteristic of the Ohio campaign of that year. He might attribute the high turnout, for example, to an assumed charismatic quality of the Democratic gubernatorial candidate, Martin L. Davey, the late tree surgeon. If one examines, however, the 1934 mid-term dip in turnout in other states, he finds that everywhere the decline was relatively small. The relatively high 1934 vote in Ohio then can more probably be attributed to factors common to all states and not simply to those peculiar to Ohio. (A similar check could be made to determine the validity of the explanation above of the relatively small slump in Ohio turnout in 1950. Was this a phenomenon peculiar to Ohio, or did it occur in other states with or without senatorial elections in that year?) The general rule might be that when the situation under examination is a part of a larger whole, the prudent inquirer asks whether the apparent peculiarities of the special situation may not in reality be attributes of the entirety. This question is almost invariably relevant in the examination of political subdivisions.

## Time Series and Unique Events

In many instances the finding from a time series comes not from its pattern of uniformities or from the deviations from that pattern but from the fact that the graph of the series constitutes an arresting presentation of a unique event or complex of events. The use of a series for describing or thinking about such an event involves no statistical analysis; it merely amounts to a description quantitative in form because of the nature of the data. The interpretation of such a single series is by the ordinary tools of logical analysis and not by the methods of statistics.

Illustrative is Figure 12, which indicates the proportion of the citizen population 21 and over voting in Texas before and after the adoption of the poll tax. The curve might be examined to test the hypothesis that the poll tax accounts for the low level of electoral participation in the state. The feature of the graph that first attracts attention is the fact that turnout began to decline abruptly after the peak strength of Populism in the state in 1896

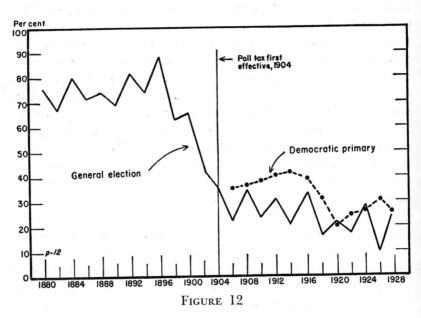

FIGURE 12

*The Poll Tax and Voter Turnout: Percentage of Citizens 21 Years of Age and Over Voting in Texas General Elections for Governor, 1880–1928, and in Democratic Primaries, 1906–1928*

and continued to fall until the election of 1904 when payment of the poll tax was for the first time a prerequisite to voting. After that date the proportion of the eligibles voting tended to level off.

Since the major drop in popular interest in voting occurred before the inauguration of the poll-tax requirement, one may conclude that some factor or complex of factors other than the tax was at the bottom of most of the precipitous decline in popular participation, although the tax may well have helped to hold participation at a low level after the initial drop. One question is answered only to raise others. Indeed, the most definitive results of systematic inquiry often consist in the elimination of plausible but incorrect explanations. By continued testing, hypotheses that do not fit the facts may be rejected. Whether the correct explanation can be found is another question, but at least some erroneous ones may be avoided.

*Hazards in Interpretation of Series*

One of the major hazards in the interpretation of time series arises from the relative brevity of the available political series. Special caution must always be exercised in drawing inferences from short series. The hazards and the possibilities of avoiding them may be seen from the example provided in Figures 13 and

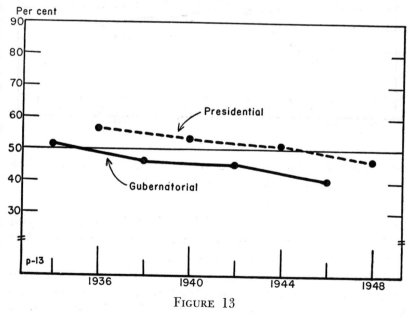

FIGURE 13

*Democratic Percentage of Two-Party Vote for Governor and President, Pennsylvania, 1934–1948*

14. In Figure 13 the Democratic percentages of the major-party vote for President and for governor in Pennsylvania are graphed for the period 1934 to 1948. From the fact that the gubernatorial elections are held in the off-years and have a uniformly lower Democratic proportion of the vote than in the presidential polling, the generalization might be made that the lower turnout in the off years invariably creates a differential against the Democrats. Therefore, all good Democrats should try to amend the state con-

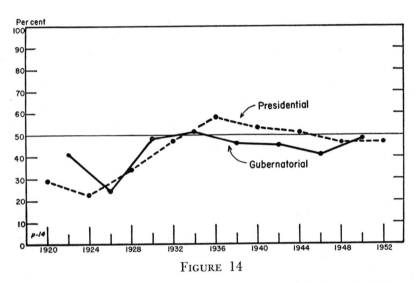

FIGURE 14

*Democratic Percentage of Two-Party Presidential and Gubernatorial Vote, Pennsylvania, 1920–1952*

stitution to schedule gubernatorial elections simultaneously with the presidential; and, for the same reason, all good Republicans should attempt to retain the *status quo*.

Such a generalization may well describe the short term accurately, but before one commits himself to so broad an interpretation he would be prudent to extend the series as far back as practicable. From the evidence in Figure 14, which presents the same series for the period 1920–1950, some generalization other than that suggested by the shorter series obviously is in order. In the 1920's, when the Republicans were in power nationally, the Democratic proportion of the Pennsylvania gubernatorial vote tended to exceed the Democratic proportion of the presidential vote. Examination of a sufficient number of cases could provide the basis for a broader, but still tentative, generalization that would take into account all the data. If, for example, the party in the minority nationally tended to have a higher vote in gubernatorial votes in off-year elections, any adjustment of the elections calendar would give one party only a short-term advantage, if it is assumed that the pattern represents a behavior that will continue. Whatever the explanation, the descriptive generalization suggested by the shorter series in Figure 13 needs qualification.

In surmising the meaning of time series the cautious observer may avoid pitfalls at times by breaking down the aggregate involved in a series. When a series can be broken into components, it is well to determine whether such a break-down might alter an interpretation suggested by the total. Thus, two points in a series on the Democratic percentage of the total presidential popular vote in the United States are:

|  | 1944 | 1948 |
|---|---|---|
| United States | 53.4% | 49.4% |

On this basis statements were made such as, "The general drift of American voters from the socialism of the Fair Deal toward the doctrines of sound Republicanism from 1944 to 1948 foreshadows a rout of the Democrats in 1952." A more restrained interpretation was, "Electoral sentiment shifted away from the Democratic party from 1944 to 1948." Yet even that remark was not completely accurate. If the aggregative series is broken into its components, a different picture emerges. By this means one may identify some of the complexities, or at least be guided toward qualifications, in description of the total trend. Thus some of the state components of the national series on Democratic percentage of the total vote moved contrary to the drift of the total:

|           | 1944   | 1948   |
|-----------|--------|--------|
| Iowa      | 47.5%  | 50.3%  |
| Indiana   | 46.7   | 48.8   |
| Minnesota | 52.4   | 57.2   |

When one works with figures on aggregates, i.e., figures that relate to classes or groups of units, it is prudent to keep in mind the question whether interpretations drawn from or about the total would be confirmed or modified by examination of information, if available, on subdivisions of the aggregate under inspection.

### 3. Analysis of Time Series: Measurement of Dispersion

In many situations the inferences that may be drawn from a simple graph of a time series provide as exact and satisfactory an interpretation as can be made of the data. In other instances one may desire to measure or to describe in mathematical terms the characteristics of the series appearing on the graph. If, for example, one wishes to compare the magnitudes of the fluctuation of a pair of series around their central values, a precise measurement of the fluctuation of each series is required. Measures of dispersion, which have already been described, may be used in dealing with this problem. An illustration of their application to time series will serve to illustrate further the nature of these measures and to indicate one means of analyzing time series.

Students of politics become concerned about the magnitude of the movements of voters from party to party. Election figures do not tell us much about this phenomenon because they show only the net shift of strength. One party has a larger proportion of the vote at one election than it did at the preceding polling. To get a line on the gross shift, that is, those moving in both directions, one has to rely on sample surveys. Yet election statistics are about all the data we have. One method of sifting something from the data with respect to electoral volatility is to apply measures of dispersion. Consider the following pair of series indicating the Democratic percentage of the two-party vote for governor and for President, respectively, in Ohio for the period 1900–1950:

| PER CENT DEMOCRATIC FOR GOVERNOR | | PER CENT DEMOCRATIC FOR PRESIDENT | |
|---|---|---|---|
| | | 1900 | 46.6% |
| 1901 | 45.8% | | |
| 1903 | 43.2 | | |
| | | 1904 | 36.5 |
| 1905 | 52.4 | | |
| 1908 | 50.9 | 1908 | 46.8 |
| 1910 | 55.9 | | |
| 1912 | 61.7 | 1912 | 60.4 |
| 1914 | 48.6 | | |
| 1916 | 50.3 | 1916 | 54.0 |
| 1918 | 50.6 | | |
| 1920 | 46.9 | 1920 | 39.8 |
| 1922 | 50.5 | | |
| 1924 | 54.5 | 1924 | 28.9 |
| 1926 | 50.6 | | |
| 1928 | 44.9 | 1928 | 34.7 |
| 1930 | 52.8 | | |
| 1932 | 54.1 | 1932 | 51.5 |
| 1934 | 51.5 | | |
| 1936 | 52.1 | 1936 | 60.8 |
| 1938 | 47.6 | | |
| 1940 | 44.5 | 1940 | 52.2 |
| 1942 | 39.5 | | |
| 1944 | 51.8 | 1944 | 49.8 |
| 1946 | 49.1 | | |
| 1948 | 53.7 | 1948 | 50.1 |
| 1950 | 52.6 | | |

When these two series are graphed, they take the forms shown in Figure 15. Inspection of the graphs suggests that there is a wider swing in the party division of the presidential vote than in the gubernatorial vote. By what method may the amplitude of the fluctuation of the two series be measured and compared? Measures of dispersion may be applied in the analysis of the type of series under examination. They provide a notion of the scatter of the cases of a series around some point indicative of central tendency—the mean, median, or mode.

The range is the most simple and most easily computed measure of dispersion. It is simply the difference between the highest number and the lowest number of the series. For the Ohio gubernatorial data the range is 22.2 per cent, that is, the difference between the highest Democratic percentage, 61.7 in 1912, and the lowest, 39.5 in 1942. The other items of the series fall between these two extremes. For the presidential series the range is 31.9

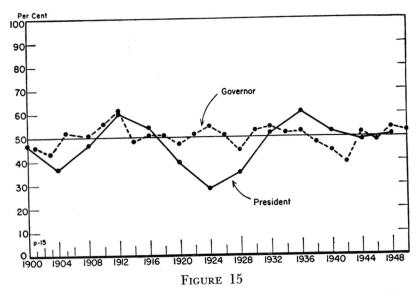

FIGURE 15

*Democratic Percentage of Two-Party Vote for Governor and for President, Ohio, 1900–1950*

per cent, which is the difference between the peak Democratic percentage of 60.8 in 1936 and the low of 28.9 in 1924. At times the range has its uses, but in comparisons between series the range may be quite misleading. One extreme case added to a series may change the range considerably without affecting materially the spread of the rest of the cases around the mean.

In the preceding chapter the application of the average deviation to the measurement of the dispersion of frequency series was illustrated and the limitations of this measure were set out. The same measure, which is, it will be recalled, the mean of the deviations of the items of a series from the mean of all the cases, may be used in the measurement of the fluctuations of certain types of time series. The data on Ohio presidential and gubernatorial elections, although consisting of observations at scattered points through time, may be treated as frequency distributions. If one traverses the steps for calculation laid out in the preceding chapter, he finds that the average or mean deviation of the Ohio gubernatorial data from the mean of the series, 50.2 per cent, is 3.38. This gives a measure of the dispersion of the individual election percentages around the mean percentage. The average deviation of the presidential series is 7.57 from a mean of 47.1 per cent. The average deviation of the presidential series is, thus, more than twice the size of that for the gubernatorial data.

To compare the measures of dispersion of different distributions, as was indicated in the preceding chapter, one must convert them into coefficients or measures of relative dispersion for reasons akin to those that lead us to convert absolute figures into percentages of their respective wholes for purposes of comparison. Happily or unhappily for our illustrative purposes the average deviations just presented are comparable in their raw form for limited purposes. Since the original data are in percentages, the average deviations may be directly compared, although not as an ordinary use of these measures. Thus, it might be said that all the factors that produced shifts in the two-party division over the period—the crossing of party lines, differential success in attraction of new voters, differential effects of third-party candidates, and so forth—had the net result of affecting about twice as large a proportion—7.57 against 3.38—of those voting in presidential elections as in the gubernatorial elections, all as measured by the average deviation.

Such a comparison is, of course, feasible only because the original data were in percentages. If the original data had been in absolute numbers instead of percentages, the average deviations would have had to be translated into coefficients or measures of relative deviation to produce any sort of comparability.[6] The more conventional procedure is to convert the measure of deviation into a relative measure. Suppose that it is wished to compare the fluctuations of the Democratic percentage of the gubernatorial vote around its mean with the dispersion of the presidential percentage around its mean. A coefficient of deviation, as has been indicated in the preceding chapter, is simply the percentage that the average deviation is of the mean from which the deviation occurs. Thus, in the case of the gubernatorial data, with a mean of 50.2 and an average deviation of 3.38:

$$\frac{3.38}{50.2} = .0673$$

Multiplication by 100 produces, for easier handling, a coefficient of 6.73. The application of the same formula to the presidential series results in a coefficient of 16.07. The average dispersion of the gubernatorial percentage around its mean was 6.73 per cent of the mean Democratic percentage, whereas the average deviation of the presidential series amounted to 16.07 per cent of the mean of that series. Thus, no matter what the size or form of the average deviations may be, conversion to coefficients puts them into a comparable form. Our particular average deviations were comparable in their raw form only in a very limited and rather special sense.

The standard deviation, as has been observed, is in far better odor as a measure of dispersion than is the average deviation. The standard deviation, it will be recalled, is obtained by squaring the deviations from the mean of the series, obtaining the mean of these squares, and then extracting the square root of this mean. The literal execution of this procedure is quite a chore. By the use of a table of squares or a calculator the standard deviation ($\sigma$) can be obtained rather easily by use of the following computational formula:

[6] In the instance of the particular illustration, however, it would not be sensible to use absolute figures because of the long-term upward trend in the size of the vote. Measures of dispersion have no utility in the analysis of time series unless the series tends to fluctuate around a central value. If the series indicates, for example, a long-term secular trend, other types of analysis would be in order.

$$\sigma = \sqrt{\frac{\Sigma X^2}{N} - \left(\frac{\Sigma X}{N}\right)^2}$$

Here $X$ equals an item in the series. The symbol $\Sigma$ is read as "the sum of." Thus $\Sigma X^2$ equals the sum of the squares of the individual items in the series. $\Sigma X$ is the sum of all the items in the series. $N$ is the number of items.

To apply the formula to the Ohio presidential data requires the preparation of a table with two columns, one headed $X$ and the other $X^2$. Thus,

|  | $X$ | $X^2$ |
|---|---|---|
| 1900 | 46.6 | 2171.56 |
| 1904 | 36.5 | 1332.25 |

And so on through the series to produce a total for $X$ of 612.1 and a total for $X^2$ of 29,945.3. Substitutions would then be made in the above formula:

$$\sigma = \sqrt{\frac{29,945.3}{13} - \left(\frac{612.1}{13}\right)^2}$$
$$= \sqrt{2,303.5 - 2,217.0}$$
$$= \sqrt{86.5}$$
$$= 9.3$$

To save labor, it may be in order to note that most statistics texts have a table of square roots in the appendix.

Another computational formula, which postpones division until the final step, reduces erraticism in the final results from the exercise of capricious judgment in the lopping off of decimals in the earlier stages of the operation. It is as follows:

$$\frac{\sqrt{N\Sigma X^2 - (\Sigma X)^2}}{N}$$

When a series consists of a large number of items, calculation of the standard deviation is simplified by grouping the items into a frequency table and by computation from the table instead of from the raw data, that is, from all the individual items of the series. The procedure is set out in most elementary statistics texts.

As with the average deviation, the standard deviation may be reduced to a coefficient for comparative purposes. In the illustrative cases, since the original data are in percentages, the standard deviations themselves may be compared directly with respect to some questions bearing on the entire body of voters. To compare the variability of the Democratic segment of the total vote for the presidency and the governorship, one must use a measure of relative variation. The coefficient of variation, which may be represented by the letter $V$, is the standard deviation as a percentage of the mean designated here by $\overline{X}$:

$$V = \frac{\sigma}{\overline{X}} \times 100$$

If the mean and standard deviation of the gubernatorial data are substituted in the formula, we have:

$$V = \frac{4.47}{50.2} \times 100$$
$$= 8.90$$

And for the presidential data the result is 19.7. Thus the ups and downs in the presidential vote, as measured by the standard deviation, travel over a much larger proportion of the mean of the presidential series than do the fluctuations of the gubernatorial vote in relation to its mean.

How much further ahead is one when he determines that the coefficient of variation of the gubernatorial series is 8.9; that of the presidential series, 19.7? If the analysis stops at that point, the answer is, probably not much. Broad differences in two types of electoral behavior have been identified and assigned numerical values. The descriptive import of those numerical values may be interpreted in the light of the explanation given in the preceding chapter. Thus, about two thirds of the gubernatorial votes fall within plus or minus 8.9 per cent of their mean and a similar proportion of the presidential votes fall within plus or minus 19.7 per cent of their mean. Yet the significance and the factors associated with the types of behavior identified must be sought by both insight and more intensive analysis. Is the electorate more responsible to the pulls of national campaigns than to the issues of state politics? Do the state organizations command a loyalty and a vote-getting apparatus that enable them to resist somewhat the great tides of opinion that sweep the nation and move numbers of people from party to party or to the support of minor presidential candidates? Or are the differences insignificant? Or is the difference attributable to the greater variation of the presidential campaign (than the state) in pulling voters to the polls? Only when the particular data are thought about in relation to hypotheses of some import do they take on meaning. And quite often such reflections lead to further inquiry rather than to an immediate answer.

## Limits to Analysis of Time Series by Measurement of Dispersion

A technical limitation on the use of measures of dispersion to estimate the amplitude of fluctuations in time series needs to be emphasized. As has been noted in earlier pages, time series may be characterized by a secular trend reflecting a more or less long-term movement upward or downward. They may also fluctuate in cycles characterized by a more or less uniform periodicity. A single series may manifest both cyclical and secular characteristics. The series in Figure 10 on page 35 is such a series, whereas the two Ohio series in Figure 15 on page 46 contain virtually no element of trend but rather reflect almost solely cyclical or short-term fluctuations.

Obviously the use of the standard deviation to measure the dispersion of the items in a time series such as that in Figure 10 around the mean of the series would measure a dispersion accounted for by both secular trend and short-term fluctuations. The vertical spread of the items in the series is accounted for to a considerable degree by the trend. On the other hand, the standard deviation of the items of either of the Ohio series around their mean would measure by and large a dispersion accounted for by short-term variations.

If the object is to measure the dispersion of short-term variations and a series has a noticeable trend element in it, as does the series in Figure 10, the trend must be removed from the series before measuring dispersion. The broken line in Figure 10 is known as the line of regression and is fitted by the method of least squares, a procedure to be explained at a later point. To "remove the trend" from a series a line of regression is fitted. The measurement of dispersion then becomes a matter of measuring the spread of the items of the series around this line. One thus obtains a measure of short-term fluctuations with the effect of the trend on the dispersion of the items removed from the calculations.

There occur in political data many time series that contain little or no secular trend. Such series usually reflect some sort of phenomena in which fluctuations occur about a more or less stable level of equilibrium. In those cases calculation of dispersion without removal of whatever slight trend may appear in the series is both a matter of convenience and a realistic estimate of the character of the data. Thus in the two Ohio series in Figure 15 the presidential series manifests a slight upward trend and the gubernatorial series a slight downward trend. Neither of these trends is visible to the naked eye as is the trend in the series in Figure 10. The removal of the trends in the Ohio series would produce no change in the types of inferences that might be made from the findings. The average deviation from the line of regression of the presidential series is 7.1 in comparison with an average deviation of 7.57 from the mean. The average deviation of the gubernatorial series turned out to be 3.38 from either the mean or the line of regression so slight was the trend element.

## 4. Series of Complex Measurements

The examples of time series cited thus far have involved only the recording of the changing values of a single variable at regular intervals in time. Fluctuations in the Republican percentage of the vote in Brown County, changes in the proportion of the potential electorate of Ohio turning out to the polls, and other such series all consist of single variables that change through time. In dealing with some types of data and some types of problems the time dimension may be extremely significant, but the student is puzzled about how to reduce the more or less complex data concerning the phenomenon at each point in time to a manageable form. In such situations he often finds fruitful the use of a time series whose individual units consist of measurements of many variables or relationships among variables at separated points in time. By this means a mass of data may often be converted into a simple time series both meaningful and comprehensible.

If the problem concerns, for example, the behavior of many related time series, construction of a time series of the means or averages of the individual items at intervals in time may prove helpful. Or the series may consist of some other measure of central tendency. Thus the data might consist of the earnings figures for a thousand individual clerks over a period of years. Reams of such data could be compressed into a series showing the average earnings of the thousand clerks from time period to time period. In all such operations, of course, the uses and limitations of whatever measure is incorporated into the series must be kept in mind. For example, a time series of median earnings might be more useful for some purposes than one of mean earnings.

An illustrative example appears in Figure 16. The problem was to identify counties in Ohio with a long-term increase in Democratic strength and to discern, if possible, something of the nature of the process of party realignment or at least to be able to raise relevant questions about its nature. The data consisted of figures on the Democratic percentage of the two-party vote in each of the 88 counties for each of the presidential elections from 1920 through 1952. The voting behavior of each county could be traced through 32 years, but the tabulation of 792 figures was both meaningless and confusing. The manipulations to pull some meaning out of the mass of data are recorded in Figure 16. Ten counties in 1952 had a Democratic percentage of the two-party vote 10 points or more higher than in 1920. The mean of the Democratic percentages in these counties was computed for each of the elections, with the results shown in the chart. Alongside this series was placed the mean percentage for all the counties for each election.[7]

The graphs in Figure 16 thus reduce 792 figures to a simple form and permits some speculation about the process of party realignment. Evidently, at least in this instance, realignment or

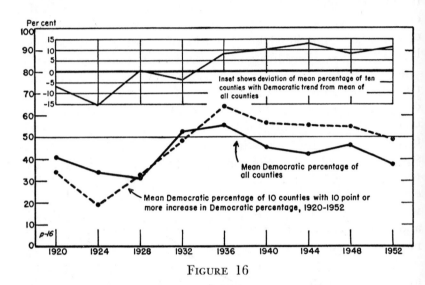

FIGURE 16

*Party Realignment, 1920–1952: Mean Democratic Percentage of Two-Party Presidential Vote for All Ohio Counties and for Ten Counties with 10 Point or More Increase in Democratic Percentage from 1920 to 1952*

shift in the ten counties occurred by stages. Our ten counties apparently were more responsive than the rest of the state to the LaFollette appeal in 1924; their Democratic percentage of the two-party vote dropped sharply. In 1928 the Democrats made gains in these counties while the mean of all counties moved toward Hoover and the Republicans. In 1936 the ten-county Demo-

[7] The averaging of percentages has its hazards. In these cases the object was to indicate the mean net percentage shift in partisan preference of the voting units. Such a mean percentage differs, of course, from the percentage division of the vote of the state as a whole or of the entire vote of the ten counties. If one were concerned with the relative size or importance of the vote of the ten counties in the state as a whole, other types of calculations would be in order.

cratic trend continued. In 1940 the mean of these counties leveled out and continued to move at a point above the mean for all counties. The process of party realignment thus may occur in a series of cumulative steps all of which may reflect a complex inter-action between party appeals, group interests, economic trends, the inertia of traditional attachments, and other factors. This type of analysis, of course, merely outlines the broad tendencies and creates a springboard from which more intensive analyses may be launched.[8]

By way of lagniappe the inset in Figure 16 illustrates another trick of analysis. The single curve in the inset represents the trend of the mean of our ten counties with the mean of all the counties treated as zero. Or, it represents the deviation of the mean of the ten counties from the mean of all counties with heed paid to the signs. Implicit in this type of presentation is an assumption that the voters of all counties behaved in response to common influences, but that additional special influences or factors were at work in the deviant counties. By the calculation of the deviations and their presentation as in the inset one perhaps obtains a rough measure of the net effects of these special influences or factors.

The use of the mean or the average in a time series represents a simple but useful operation. In other instances series constructed of measurements of dispersion, rather than measures of central tendency, may provide a method for attacking a problem or of presenting data. In the preceding chapter, for example, the dis-persion of voting units of Wayne County in their partisan division of the vote was used to illustrate the nature of the standard devia-tion. A time series over a considerable period indicating variations in such a dispersion might offer instructive insights into the chang-ing nature of party cleavages when interpreted in the light of other data. In the instance of the earnings of the thousand clerks, for some purposes a time series built up of measures of dispersion might be useful. In still other situations, series built up of coeffi-cients of correlation (to be explained at a later point) may be used to analyze changes through time in the relationships between two

[8] The counties with a Democratic trend as defined were: Ashtabula, Belmont, Cuyahoga, Jefferson, Lake, Lorain, Lucas, Mahoning, Summit, Trumbull.

sets of variables. Thus, if through time the correlation of the county-by-county percentage of the vote for Republican candidates for President with the percentage of the vote for Republican candidates for governor declines, increases, varies, or remains stable, various inferences become possible about the nature of party organization and party loyalty.

## References

### *Method*

Edward R. Dewey and Edwin F. Dakin, *Cycles, The Science of Prediction* (Holt, 1947).

John E. Freund, *Modern Elementary Statistics* (Prentice-Hall, 1952), chap. 19.

Frederick C. Mills, *Statistical Methods* (Holt, rev. ed., 1938), Chap. 7, "The Analysis of Time Series: Measurement of Trend," Chap. 8, "The Analysis of Time Series: Measurement of Seasonal and Cyclical Fluctuation."

Simon Kuznets, "Time Series," *Encyclopaedia of the Social Sciences.*

M. J. Moroney, *Facts from Figures* (Penguin Books, 1951), Chap. 17, "Time Series and Fortune Telling."

Albert E. Waugh, *Elements of Statistical Method* (McGraw-Hill, 3rd ed., 1952), Chap. 13, "Historical Data."

### *Applications*

Louis H. Bean, *How to Predict Elections* (Knopf, 1948). This book carries an incidental but important methodological lesson for beginning students who often contrive techniques that are both incomprehensible and far more complex than the problem warrants. Mr. Bean, a statistician of very considerable virtuosity, in this book nowhere indulges in statistical display but uses simple and understandable techniques appropriate to the data and problems.

————, *The Mid-Term Battle* (Washington: Cantillon Books, 1950).

Hadley Cantril, *Gauging Public Opinion* (Princeton University Press, 1944), Chap. 16, "The Use of Trends."

Samuel J. Eldersveld, "The Influence of Metropolitan Party Pluralities in Presidential Elections since 1920," *American Political Science Review,* 43 (1949), 1189–1206.

C. A. M. Ewing, *Presidential Elections* (Norman: University of Oklahoma Press, 1940).

————,*Congressional Elections,* 1896–1944 (Norman: University of Oklahoma Press, 1947).

Ralph and Mildred Fletcher, "Consistency of Party Voting from 1896–1932," *Social Forces,* 15 (1936), pp. 281–285.

Robert E. Lane, "Government Regulation and the Business Mind," *American Sociological Review,* 16 (1951), pp. 163–173.

Malcolm Moos, *Politics, Presidents, and Coattails* (Baltimore: Johns Hopkins Press, 1952).

S. S. Nilson, "Mechanics and Historical Laws," *Journal of Philosophy,* 48 (1951), pp. 201–211.

James K. Pollock, *The Direct Primary in Michigan* (Ann Arbor: Bureau of Government, University of Michigan, 1943).

Stuart A. Rice, *Quantitative Methods in Politics* (Knopf, 1928), Part VI.

C. H. Titus, *Voting Behavior in the United States* (Berkeley: University of California Press, 1935).

# 3

## INTERRELATIONSHIPS OF
## TIME SERIES

The simple inspection of single time series, as was demonstrated in the preceding chapter, often permits a rough and ready interpretation of some phenomena of political significance. Another kind of problem of analysis is presented, however, by the concern of political scientists and historians with the relationships between two variables through time. When the examination of political phenomena in its time dimension gets beyond chronology, the hypothesis recurs that a particular trend or set of variations in political behavior may be "caused" or associated with some related political or "non-political" trend or set of variations. The formula of reasoning is common among historical and political writers who are often unaware of the essentially quantitative nature of their reasoning. Thus, "The movement toward democratization of political practices and institutions gained momentum from the effects of the westward movement." Implicit in such a statement is a series more or less measuring the growth of "democratization," which is affected by another equally impalpable variable, "the westward movement." Or, "Representative government came to creak and groan under the strains imposed by industrialization." Here some sort of index of efficiency of government is related to ome measure of the complex of forces under the umbrella of industrialization.

Such descriptions of the interactions of vast and complex factors have to be made and ordinarily have to be made impressionistically. Yet when the political series and the supposedly causal factor can be put into quantitative form, such problems of the relationships of variables can be attacked by comparison, through methods of varying precision and intricacy, of the relationships between the two series through time. Thus, we have, for example, the hypothesis that prosperity assures victory for the party in power, whereas a downswing in the curve of business activity makes probable an increase in the vote for the outs. By the use of measures of economic well being and elections series, the relationship between two such variables can be determined. In other instances questions arise concerning relationships that involve no hypothesis of the existence of a "causal" relation. Is the partisan division within Florida becoming more similar to that of the country as a whole? Do the popular votes for President and for candidates for the House of Representatives fluctuate together? To many such questions involving relations between pairs of series the same techniques of analysis may be used as is applied to the measurement of supposedly causal relations between series.

## Inspection of Paired Series

For many purposes a simple graphing of the pair of time series is adequate to determine the nature of the relationship between two variables. The character of their relationships can often be ascertained accurately enough by visual inspection of the pattern revealed by the chart. This crude sort of treatment has the virtue of simplicity in both execution and presentation, and perhaps in dealing with many types of data the results are in reality as precise as might be obtained by more complex analysis.

## "Causal" Relations

When two series fluctuate in unison through time, the easy conclusion is that the changes in the variable represented by one of the series caused the variations in the other. That conclusion may,

of course, be quite incorrect. In forming the judgment that seri
B would not have fluctuated had series A remained stable (an
other factors stayed constant), we find that elements not recorde
on the chart enter into the logical process. At later points we sha
return to this problem, but for the moment consider the illustr
tion of the use of paired graphs to test a supposed causal relatio

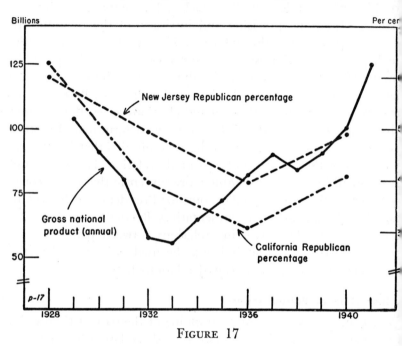

FIGURE 17

*Depression and the Fate of the Republicans: Republican Percen
age of Two-Party Presidential Vote, New Jersey and Californi
1928–1940, and Annual Gross National Product, 1929–1941*

between two series in Figure 17. That chart contains curves ind
cating the Republican percentage of the two-party presidenti
vote in New Jersey and California, 1928–1940, and another curv
representing the fluctuations in gross national product over th
period 1929–1941. The various series move roughly in the sam
directions and illustrate the relation of depression and recovery t
the Republican vote in these states, at least for the period co

red. The use of series that are built on such heterogeneous aggregates as the votes of states and the national product, of course, does
not reveal many other relevant factors. A procedure such as that
represented in Figure 17 can suggest the existence of a broad type
of relationship, but more precise analysis would employ series for
smaller territorial units and finer measures of shifts in economic
well-being to test the relation between prosperity and party for-
unes. Care is required in the interpretation of the relations shown
o exist by even such simple methods. Over the elections covered
by the chart it seems evident that matters in addition to level of
business activity had a hand in the shifting of voter loyalties. Furthermore, it is evident that improvement of business conditions
does not always increase the popular support of the party in
power. Nor do charts such as Figures 17 and 22 (on page 70)
reveal anything about the closeness of the relationship between
the compared series. When two different scales are used on an
arithmetic chart to accommodate series in different units (such as
Republican percentages and billions of dollars, as in Figure 17)
the scales may be adjusted to make it appear that the two series
move up and down in close association. The possibility of convey-
ng an erroneous visual impression of closeness of association
makes this type of chart suspect. The utility of this sort of chart,
hence, rests solely in its demonstration whether two series move
n the same direction from point to point in time rather than as
an indication that they are functionally related, i.e., for example,
that a decline of so many billions in national income brings with
t a drop of so many points in Republican percentage of the vote.
When the problem is to compare rates of change as well as direc-
ions of movement of two series, semi-logarithmic charts, to be
described later in this chapter, are often useful.

The inclusion of graphs for the votes of two states in the illus-
ration gives it an analytical characteristic that should be specifi-
ally mentioned. Note that the curves for the votes of New Jersey
and California move, at least grossly, in the same manner. The
act that both behave similarly in relation to the business trend
gives special plausibility to the inferred causal relation, if we as-
ume that the impact of the business trend was the same on both

states. The reasoning represents a rough application of Mill's method of agreement which he put as follows: "If two or more instances of the phenomenon under investigation have only one circumstance in common, the circumstance in which alone all the instances agree is the cause (or effect) of the given phenomenon." Had the votes of the two states moved in opposite directions, it would have been concluded that business fluctuations had nothing to do with the electoral variations or possibly that in one instance another determinant offset their effect. Another way of thinking about *only* two time series, the New Jersey vote and the national product series, for example, is to suppose that each point in time is an instance "of the phenomenon under investigation." If the two series fluctuate together at each point in time (i.e., the separate instances "have only one circumstance in common"), a causal relation becomes plausible but, as will be indicated later, is not "proved." The difficulty rests in establishing that the different instances have only one circumstance in common. The general method, however, provides a firmer basis for excluding supposedly but actually unrelated factors.

Another sort of hypothesis about "causal" relations may be tested by the inspection of paired graphs. The behavior of two entities through time may be compared to check the supposition that some difference between them is associated with a difference in their political behavior in response to events or factors not readily quantifiable. A specific application, to test the supposition that German-Americans were driven from the Democratic party by the Roosevelt policy toward Germany before 1940 and by the war itself in 1944, appears in the graphs in Figure 18. The chart shows a precipitous decline in Democratic strength in Chatfield Township of Crawford County, Ohio, from 1936 to 1944. The Democrats lost far more strength relatively in the township than they did in the county as a whole or in the state. From a map showing land ownership in the county in 1894, the names alone indicated that Chatfield Township was about the most German area in the county. Such names as the following appeared as farm owners: Benjamin Zucker, Gotleib Lust, Jacob Fox, Daniel Schneider, Frederick Hipp, John Burger, Michael Schnarenberger, Peter

Bauer, George Heiser, George Stahl, Adam Lutz, Peter Geiger, Jacob Fauser, Jacob Durr, Peter Zimmerman, John Burgbacher.[1] Even today, inquiry reveals, the township neighborhood is inelegantly alluded to in the non-Teutonic society of Bucyrus, the county seat, as "Krautville." In 1940 the township went over to Willkie and in 1944 it gave Dewey an even larger vote. In 1948 it

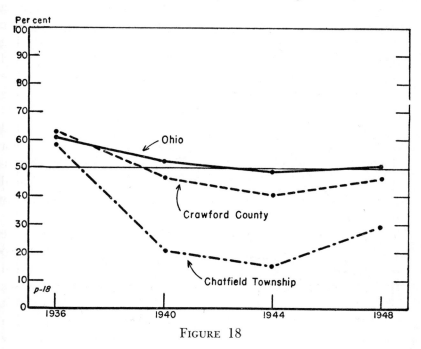

FIGURE 18

*Democratic Percentage of Two-Party Presidential Vote in Ohio, Crawford County, and Chatfield Township, 1936–1948*

began a return to the Democratic party. One inference could be that the German-American group in 1940 and 1944 lacked enthusiasm for Administration policy toward Germany.

To understand more clearly the general technique, one needs to differentiate this case from the instance of the depression and the Republican vote covered in Figure 17. In that instance, one variable, the national income, was related to another variable, the

[1] *1894 Atlas of Crawford County, Ohio* (place, publisher not indicated).

Republican vote. The analysis of Chatfield Township, in effect, assumes the existence of a series representing some sort of index of the compatibility of Democratic campaign appeals with the values of the German group. If such an index existed, it would presumably fluctuate in unison with the Democratic vote in the township after the fashion of the relations between the series in

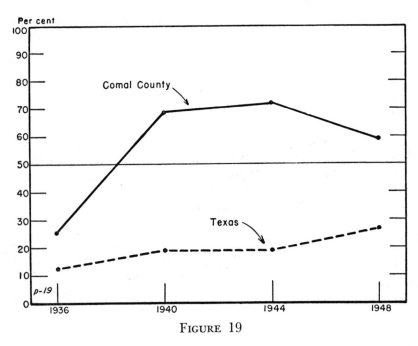

FIGURE 19

*Republican Percentage of Two-Party Presidential Vote, Texas and Comal County, 1936–1948*

Figure 18. In the absence of such a series, the type of analysis in Figure 18 has its uses.

Often a check may be made on inferences resting on procedures such as these about Chatfield Township by examining another like situation. If the same relationships do not prevail in the second instance, the initial interpretation needs re-examination. Such a check is provided in this case by the record of one of the German counties of Texas, which appears in Figure 19. Comal

County, whose county seat is New Braunfels, was originally settled by Germans. It behaved, in comparison with the rest of the state, about the same way as did Chatfield Township of Crawford County, Ohio. A sharp increase in Republican strength occurred in 1940 and 1944 after the injection into the political situation of questions of policy toward Germany.

The analytical procedure used in these cases is not "statistical" in a technical sense, but merely the application of logical methods to quantitative data. The Comal County case is essentially an application of Mill's method of difference. His statement of it reads: "If an instance in which the phenomenon under investigation occurs, and an instance in which it does not occur, have every circumstance in common save one, that one occurring in the former; the circumstance in which alone the two instances differ, is the effect, or the cause, or an indispensable part of the cause, of the phenomenon." Thus the state and the county had in common the stimuli of a campaign involving foreign policy toward Germany. Their response differed. They differed also in national origins. But before one says, it follows, therefore, that the national-origin difference accounted for the difference in electoral response, it is well to pause. The process really proves nothing in a strict sense. A third factor might be the explanation.[2] For example, the 1940 campaign had other issues. Or the Republicans might have stuffed the ballot boxes in Comal County. Or several factors may have been, probably were, operative simultaneously and influenced the direction and degree of electoral shift. All of which points toward the necessity for the utmost caution in interpretation as well as the need for imagination to conjure up for consideration all the conceivable explanations for a particular phenomenon. Furthermore, until one checks on the ground he does not know that even the most plausible explanation drawn from the figures alone has a wisp of a foundation.[3] Even then the logi-

[2] It seems fairly certain, for example, that at least part of the 1940 reaction of the German-American counties was common to rural, agricultural counties whatever their national origin.

[3] This admonition should be kept in mind by the student in thinking about most of the illustrative cases in this book. Since the student of politics so often analyzes data collected by others, he often lacks the appreciation of its meaning that comes with its actual collection. "It could very well be argued," C. E. Hawley

cian would assert that nothing had been "proved" because no way exists, in the absence of rigidly controlled experiment, to know that some other differential was not determinative. Nevertheless, the method has its workaday uses though it is well to be aware of its loopholes, for such an awareness can sharpen perception.[4]

These illustrations also suggest mention of a limitation to work with aggregate statistics. The Comal County Republican percentage, for example, rose sharply in 1940 and 1944. Whether shifts of German voters from Democratic (or non-voting) status to the Republican side of the fence accounted for the change one does not really know from the aggregate vote. The association of such shifts with populations in high degree of German origin and their absence in other populations makes the inference plausible. With data on individual voting records, gathered perhaps by a sample survey, the facts could be nailed down about the group affiliations of the shifting voters. In the absence of such data one must do as well as he can with the information he has. With a little leg work and some ingenuity, a student may do pretty well. Thus, the basic technique of Samuel Lubell's *The Future of American Politics* was essentially that outlined in the preceding pages.

## Concurrent Variations in Paired Series

To be differentiated from the quest for causal or determinative relationships is the comparison of two or more series to ascertain whether the phenomena they record move together. No supposition of a causal relation is involved, but it may be analytically or descriptively helpful to know whether the series vary concurrently.[5] They may do so from a common cause, they may simply represent different aspects of the same phenomenon, or they may be related temporally and in no other way.

---

and L. A. Dexter conclude, that we political scientists "do not as a class observe. We rely upon observations which other people have recorded for other purposes." And we thereby subject ourselves to special hazards as well as limit the range of our work.—"Recent Political Science Research in American Universities," *American Political Science Review*, 46 (1952), pp. 470–485.

[4] See Morris R. Cohen and Ernest Nagel, *An Introduction to Logic and Scientific Method* (Harcourt, Brace, 1934), Chap. 13.

[5] See, in this connection, Mill's *Logic*, Book III, Chap. 22, "Of Uniformities of Co-existence not Dependent on Causation."

An example appears in Figure 20, in which graphs show the percentage of the two-party membership of the House of Representatives won by the Democrats at each election since 1900 and also the percentage of the two-party popular vote polled by Democratic presidential candidates. From one standpoint the two series are only descriptive of a single phenomenon, two facets of which are pictured by the graphs. Broad shifts in party strength occur

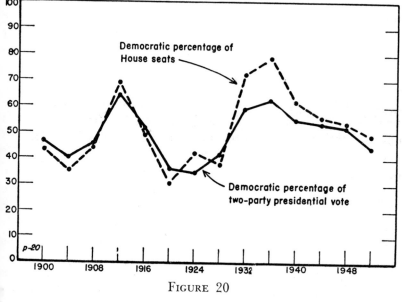

FIGURE 20

*Democratic Percentage of Two-Party Presidential Vote and of Two-Party Membership of House in Presidential Years, 1900–1952*

concurrently in each of the series. The matter could be let rest in that descriptive form, but such concurrent variations often provide a means for checking notions about matters of significance. Thus, the "personality" or the "individual appeal" of the candidate is often said to be of overweaning significance in American politics and party appeal of secondary importance. Reflection on the correlation between the two series, however, suggests that, at least in the large, party trends move the electors in the same direction in the presidential and congressional elections quite independently of personalities. To support the "personality" interpretation, in its crude form at any rate, one would have to subscribe to the notion that a strange distribution of "personality" occurs in which a superior aggregate of "personalities" happen to be nominated, both for the presidency and for Congress by first one party and then another. If party were secondary to "personality," the relation between the two series would probably be much more erratic. All this does not, of course, establish that personality is irrelevant, but it does suggest that it is not ordinarily a controlling factor in major shifts in party strength and that its role must be described in more circumscribed terms.

## Departures from Uniformity of Relation

Although significance may be attached to uniformities in fluctuation of paired time series, as in many other types of analysis of quantitative data, departures from a uniformity of relationship may be suggestive in the quest for the answers to certain types of questions. In general, it is useful, when one is puzzling about the nature of a particular event, to ask whether that event may be compared with other like events in a time series. Similarly, the relation between two events or acts may often be illuminated if they may be set in the framework of a series of pairs of relations between similar events or acts.

A sample example is provided by Figure 21, which graphs the Democratic percentage of the two-party vote for governor and President in Illinois, 1928–1948. With a couple of exceptions the two graphs move in the same direction from election to election. From 1944 to 1948 a sharp divergence in direction of movement occurred, Truman in 1948 polling a slightly smaller percentage of the vote than had Roosevelt in 1944 but Stevenson polling a substantially higher percentage of the vote for governor than had the 1944 Democratic standard bearer. The deviation shown by the graph indicates something of the vote-pulling power of Stevenson beyond that of his party and the head of the national ticket. Journalistic commentators would leave the matter at that, but the student, if he is a student, would note that the graph describes the interrelations of four variables: the vote-pulling power of Democratic and Republican candidates for both governor and President. Hence, conclusions to the effect that Stevenson had an electoral popularity enormously greater than Truman's would have to be tempered by an awareness of the possibility that Stevenson's opponent was extremely weak or that Truman's opponent was relatively strong or that both of these conditions prevailed.[6]

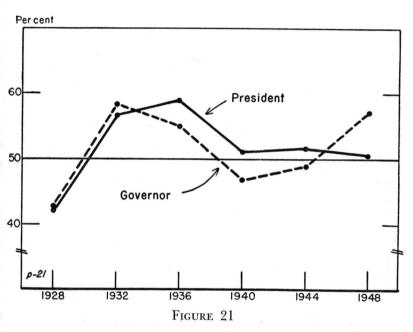

FIGURE 21

*Democratic Percentage of Two-Party Vote for Governor and for President, Illinois, 1928–1948*

The necessity for special caution in interpretation of the Illinois data comes from the fact that each graph of a percentage series represented, in effect, two series. Perhaps this is as good a spot as any to make explicit the necessity for care in the interpretation of percentage series. A graph of such a series may suggest

---

[6] See Louis Bean's *How to Predict Elections* for ingenious uses of simple measures of deviation from uniform relationships to estimate the significance of various political phenomena.

quite erroneous inferences. It invites failure to examine the underlying absolute figures. Inspect, for example, Figure 22. That chart indicates the total Democratic vote, the total Republican vote, and the Democratic percentage of the two-party vote for governor of Indiana from 1920–1948. The percentage line alone

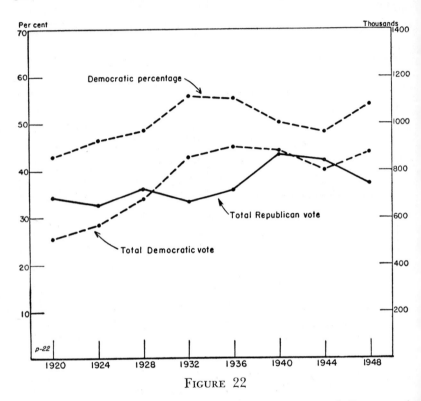

FIGURE 22

*Total Republican and Total Democratic Vote and Democratic Percentage of Two-Party Vote for Governor, Indiana, 1920–1948*

might be interpreted as a measure of the net electoral shift from party to party. If one looks, however, at the graphs on the total vote for the candidates of each party, it appears that the explanation of the variations in percentage division of the vote may have rested in considerable degree in differentials in turnout of Republicans, Democrats, and erstwhile non-voters, rather than in shifts from party to party. Or the relationship may point to relatively greater Democratic success in attracting new voters. Of course, the graphs do not establish these propositions, but they do suggest a different sort of possibility from that indicated by a graph of percentages.

*Uses of Ratio Charts*

In the comparison of two series with respect to questions on which relative rates of change are important the examination of absolute figures on an ordinary arithmetic chart may lead to erroneous conclusions. The optical illusion may be that one series fluctuates over a narrow range while the other oscillates over a range of broad amplitude. The point is illustrated by the graphs in Figure 23, showing the total Democratic vote for governor in Massachusetts and the total Democratic vote for governor in Suffolk County, Massachusetts, 1936–1950. From this pair of graphs a student, in a term paper, concluded (and the same error has often been committed by others who ought to know better) that the Suffolk County vote "has remained rather constant, compared to the fluctuations in the total state vote for the Democratic candidate. This perhaps indicates the general steadiness—or inertia?— of Suffolk County voters."

A ready and easy check on this type of interpretation—as well as a method of presenting the data—is provided by the use of semi-logarithmic paper to plot the data. On a semi-logarithmic chart the percentage rate of change of the recorded series varies with the slope from point to point (which is not the case with arithmetic charts). The steeper the slope, the higher the percentage rate of change. Furthermore, two graphs with the same percentage rate of change have the same slope on a semi-logarithmic chart without regard to their absolute size. The slope of an increase from 5 to 10 appears the same as the slope of an increase from 25 to 50. If the Massachusetts and Suffolk County voting data are plotted on semi-log paper, as in Figure 24, a different impression of the range of the fluctuations of the two series emerges than that drawn from the arithmetic chart in Figure 23. Inspection of Figure 24 indicates that the fluctuations are at about

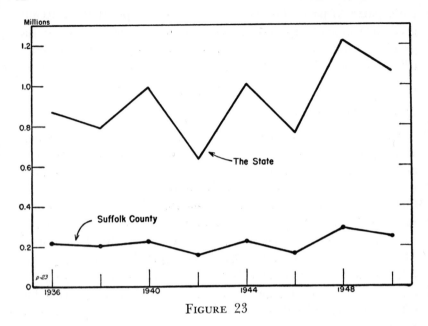

FIGURE 23

*Democratic Vote for Governor in Massachusetts: Totals for State and for Suffolk County, 1936–1950*

the same rate and that the voters of Suffolk County do not differ materially from those of the entire state, at least in this characteristic.[7] Other methods could, of course, be employed to arrive at the same conclusion, but semi-logarithmic charting permits rough comparisons of rates of change without the labor of computation.

Since the workings of the slide rule, just as do ratio charts, rest on the relationships prevailing between the logarithms of numbers, attention may be relevantly directed to the great usefulness of that simple instrument. Percentage calculations with an error of not more than one-tenth of a point can be made rapidly on a fairly good rule. Any moderately literate person can learn how to use one in a few minutes.[8]

[7] A useful brief description of the uses of semi-log charts appears in Pauline V. Young, *Scientific Social Surveys and Research* (Prentice-Hall, 2nd ed., 1949), pp. 404–412.

[8] Croxton and Cowden give brief instructions at pp. 870–871.

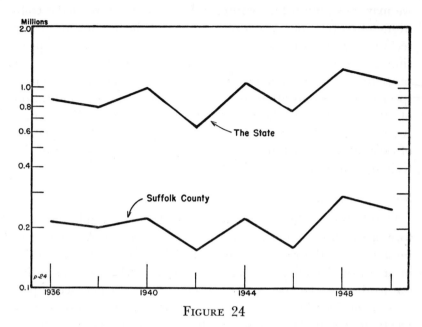

FIGURE 24

*Democratic Vote for Governor in Massachusetts: Totals for State and for Suffolk County, 1936–1950, Logarithmic Scale*

## 2. Measurement of Relation between Two Series

The preceding pages described rough-and-ready methods of identifying relationships between time series by simple inspection. For some purposes such methods yield about as certain a conclusion as can be had, and to apply more precise methods to many sorts of data would be manifestly absurd. Yet in dealing with some questions and in analyzing some types of data one needs to measure, rather than divine, the relationships between two time series.

Although the technique of correlation is usually used for other purposes, it may be applied to the measurement of the relation between a pair of time series. The coefficient of correlation, and its components, may be used to express numerically the relations that can be estimated only roughly by inspection. By easy stages we may move toward a comprehension of the nature of the technique of correlation. A pair of examples of the application of the technique to a particular type of problem in the relationships of time series will serve as a vehicle for a first look at correlation procedure. These examples, it is important to note, represent a special sort of application; they will be followed by an indication of other problems in the correlation of other types of time series. A subsequent chapter will provide a more technical explanation of correlation procedure and will illustrate the application of the technique to other types of questions.

### Scatter-Diagrams

Simply by plotting two series in parallel on a graph, one may form a rough notion of the relation between them. A more exact impression of the relation may be had by putting the two series on a scatter-diagram. The student should lend a most attentive eye to the next few pages, for, amazing though it may seem, persons of considerable intellectual endowment often profess an incapacity to comprehend a scatter-diagram. Its purpose is simple enough and its function is to put into graphic form a most ordinary pattern of reasoning. The literature of politics is replete with propositions, such as, "As international tension increases, lines of internal authority become tighter"; "A growing licentiousness among the rulers results in an increase of the spirit of rebellion among the people"; "As the size of the community increases, the sense of involvement in community affairs among the citizenry declines"; "As centralization increases, initiative at the periphery declines."

These and many other like propositions express a relation between pairs of phenomena which, if they could be expressed quantitatively, would appear as time series. In the study of politics many types of behavior may be described quantitatively in time series, and the scatter-diagram represents simply a means of presenting graphically the relation between two such series. It is also a step toward measurement to determine whether the supposed relation actually prevails and, if so, to what degree, a check to which purely verbal descriptions of associations between phenomena are not readily susceptible. Yet an understanding of the scatter-diagram and associated techniques can lead to a more cautious and prudent analysis of unquantifiable data.

Most of the pairs of time series in the preceding pages could be used to illustrate the nature of the scatter-diagram, but a new case will be introduced, which incidentally raises the question of

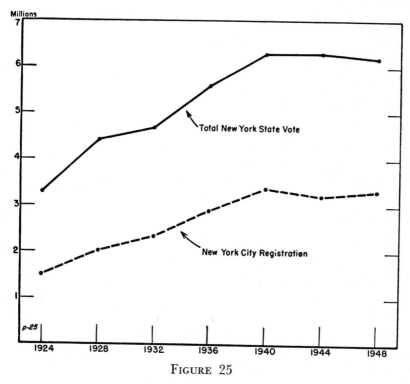

FIGURE 25

*Total New York State Presidential Vote and New York City Registration, 1924–1948*

the predictive value of relations found to exist between two time series. The relation between two series, the total registration of voters in New York City in presidential election years and the total vote for President in New York State, will be plotted on a diagram. If the relation between the registration in New York City and the vote in New York State is uniformly close, the level of city registration could be used to predict the total state turnout at the election a short time after the registration. The prediction would, of course, be no better than the assumption that a past relationship would continue to prevail.[9]

To simplify matters we shall present the two series in two ways. In Figure 25 they appear in the simple arithmetic graphic form

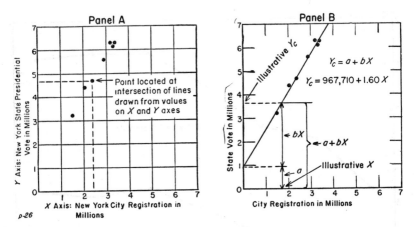

FIGURE 26

*Scatter-Diagram of Relationship between Total New York State Presidential Vote and New York City Registration, 1924–1948*

to which we have become accustomed. Obviously both series usually move in the same direction. In Figure 26 the data of the graphs are plotted as a scatter-diagram. The appearance of the diagram makes immediately apparent that some relatively uniform ratio prevails in the relation of the two series, but let us first concentrate on the panel of Figure 26 labeled A to get clearly in mind several usages in the construction of such diagrams. The

[9] The use of city rather than state registration points to a recurring peril in statistical work. Over the period covered, registration in the City was periodic and personal whereas in much of upstate New York it was non-personal. The level of City registration would probably fluctuate with the intensity of electoral interest while upstate it would tend to be less variable. The moral is that one needs to know the data he analyzes. Further, the analyst should be alert to see that the series is homogeneous over its entire length. Thus, the 1944 item in the registration series apparently is not precisely comparable with those for other years since soldier votes were cast without registration.

scale on the horizontal or $X$ axis conventionally represents the values of the so-called "independent" variable, in this case the total registration in New York City. That is, registration is the variable from which one might estimate the value of the other variable, in this case, the total vote in the state. The vertical scale or the $Y$ axis represents the values of the "dependent" variable, the total state vote.

The location of each point on the diagram is fixed at the intersection of lines drawn from the values of each pair of $X$ and $Y$ variables on their respective axes. Thus, in 1940 New York City's registration was 3,390,460 and the state's vote was 6,301,596. To represent the relation between these two values a line may be drawn from 3,390,460 on the $X$ axis and another from 6,301,596 on the $Y$ axis. A dot is placed at the intersection of these lines. Of course, the dot is placed at the point where the lines would intersect, if actually drawn. And so on for each of the other pairs of $X$ and $Y$ values in the series.

The distribution of the points on the scatter-diagram, or any distribution of points such as this on a scatter-diagram, is called a *bivariate distribution*. Note that the points in this diagram fall almost on a straight line. Where the *directionality* of scatter is a straight line rather than a curve, the relationship is called *linear*. In the case of a linear relationship of this sort a relatively uniform relation prevails between the values of $X$ and $Y$. That is, if one knows only the registration of New York City in 1928, the total state voting turnout in the presidential election later that year can be quite closely estimated, so uniform is the relation between the two variables. The closer the points to the line of directionality, the greater is the degree of association between the values of the two variables related.

Another feature of the diagram needs to be noted. In Figure 26 the line of points moves upward from left to right. This state of affairs indicates a *positive* association between the New York City registration and the New York State vote. That is, the $X$ variable is positively associated with the $Y$ variable. If one plotted on the $X$ axis of a diagram the Protestant percentage of the church membership in Massachusetts towns and on the $Y$ axis the town percentage of the 1928 presidential vote for Alfred E. Smith, whatever sort of line appeared would probably tend to slope downward from left to right. A *negative* association would be said to prevail between the two variables. That is, as the proportion of the total church membership Protestant increased from town to town, the proportion of the vote for Alfred E. Smith would decline, if the illustrative relationship assumed actually existed.

In many types of political inquiry the scatter-diagram serves as a handy tool of analysis. Without any computation beyond that necessary to produce the data for the diagram, one may by inspection of the results form judgments about the nature of the relationships existing between two variables. The direction of the relation, if any, *positive* or *negative,* is readily apparent and the closeness of the association is apparent in the degree to which the points approach a straight line. In some instances a close relationship may be of such a type that the points fall roughly along a curve. In "reading" scatter-diagrams keep in mind that when no close association exists, that fact is often a useful negative finding. Moreover, an eye for the points deviating from a distribution that would otherwise approximate linearity may often result in the illumination of particular situations. Deviations may be quite as enlightening as uniformities.

## The Line of Regression

The scatter-diagram alone provides basis for only a qualitative impression of the nature of the relation between two series. That impression is more exact than the one suggested by a pair of graphs, but it, nevertheless, remains qualitative. If we wish to measure the relationship, the characteristics of the scatter-diagram may be translated into mathematical terms. The characteristics of (a) directionality of association and (b) closeness of association may both be calculated and expressed mathematically. For the moment, attention may be centered on the question of the direction of association.

The diagonal across panel B of Figure 26, along which the points cluster, is the line of regression, which represents a statement of the directionality of the association between the two variables. One may draw such a line by eye and fairly closely approximate the line of regression, but the method of least squares may be used to locate it precisely. The line of regression is drawn so that the average of the squares of the deviations along the $Y$ axis from each of the points of the diagram to the line (i.e., the vertical distance from each of the points to the line) is at a minimum. In other words, no other straight line can be drawn through the diagram which will make the mean of the squares of the deviations along the $Y$ axis from the various points to the line any smaller than it is with this line. The mathematical problem is: Given the values of the points, how does one locate the line?

The equation for the line of regression, like the equation for any straight line,[10] can be written in the form $Y_c = a + bX$. In this equation $X$ is any one of the values of the $X$ variate and represents the abscissa (or horizontal distance from the $Y$ variate) of a given point on the line of regression. $Y_c$, called the "computed value of $Y$," is the value of the ordinate (the vertical distance from the $X$ axis) of any point on the line of regression for which the corresponding value of $X$ represents the abscissa. $a$ equals the value of $Y_c$ where the line of regression intersects the $Y$ axis or when $X$ is zero. $b$ is equal to the slope of the line or, in other words, to the ratio of the increase in $Y_c$ to the increase in $X$. The value of $Y_c$, then, is equal to the value of $a$ plus $b$ times the value of $X$. The equation, in effect, expresses a sort of average rate at which $Y$ increases or decreases with $X$. Technically, it expresses the rate at which $Y_c$ increases or decreases with $X$.

Given the equation of the straight line, the problem is to compute the values of $a$ and $b$ for the data in our diagram. The procedure of computation appears in the table below. In the column headed $X$ are placed the values of the $X$ variate, i.e., the New York City registration. (To simplify the matter the figures are given in thousands.) In the second column, headed $X^2$, are placed the squares of the registration figures. The $Y$ column consists of the values of the $Y$ variate, i.e., the New York state vote, again in

---

[10] At times the direction of the association between two variables appears not to be linear but to follow some sort of curve. In such cases a curvilinear line of regression may best fit the data.

thousands. The square of each vote total falls in the $Y^2$ column, and the $XY$ column includes the product of the registration figure for each election times the turnout for that election. (Not all of these computations are needed to locate the line of regression; they will serve another purpose within a few pages.)

| YEAR | $X$ | $X^2$ | $Y$ | $Y^2$ | $XY$ |
|---|---|---|---|---|---|
| 1924 | 1500 | 2,250,000 | 3246 | 10,536,516 | 4,869,000 |
| 1928 | 2030 | 4,120,900 | 4406 | 19,412,836 | 8,944,180 |
| 1932 | 2340 | 5,475,600 | 4689 | 21,986,721 | 10,972,260 |
| 1936 | 2900 | 8,410,000 | 5596 | 31,315,216 | 16,228,400 |
| 1940 | 3390 | 11,492,100 | 6302 | 39,715,204 | 21,363,780 |
| 1944 | 3218 | 10,355,524 | 6317 | 39,904,489 | 20,328,106 |
| 1948 | 3316 | 10,995,856 | 6177 | 38,155,329 | 20,482,932 |
| TOTALS | 18694 | 53,099,980 | 36733 | 201,026,311 | 103,188,658 |

From the totals of the above columns we obtain the values for substitution in the formulas for the computation of $a$ and $b$. The general formula for $b$ is as follows:

$$b = \frac{\Sigma XY - \dfrac{(\Sigma X)(\Sigma Y)}{N}}{\Sigma X^2 - \dfrac{(\Sigma X)^2}{N}}$$

An equivalent formula for $b$, which is a little simpler to use on a calculator equipped with automatic multiplication, is:

$$b = \frac{N\Sigma XY - (\Sigma X)(\Sigma Y)}{N\Sigma X^2 - (\Sigma X)^2}$$

For $a$ the general formula is:

$$a = \frac{\Sigma Y - b\Sigma X}{N}$$

For the data in our example, $a$ equals 967,710 (or 967.71 in thousands as the computations have been carried out) and $b$ equals

1.6026.[11] The problem becomes one of how to draw the line of regression, now that we have the values of $a$ and $b$. All that is necessary is to compute the value of two points on the line by substitution of known values in the formula, $Y_c = a + bX$. One point can be fixed readily without computation. If $X$ equals 0, then $Y_c$ equals the value of $a$, or 967,710. The value of $Y_c$ at the point where the line of regression crosses the zero line of the $X$ variate is 967,710; that point is checked off on the graph paper. To locate the second point, simply calculate $Y_c$ for any other value of $X$. If $X$ equals 3,000,000, then $Y_c$ equals 967,710 plus 1.6026 times 3,000,000, or 5,775,510. This gives a second point, which is checked off at the intersection of a line drawn vertically from 3,000,000 on the $X$ axis and another drawn horizontally from 5,775,510 on the $Y$ axis. Connect the two points to draw the line of regression.

The computation of the values for the line of regression results in a mathematical measurement and expression of the directionality of association apparent from the diagram. The line, as drawn in panel B of Figure 26, expresses in graphic form the equation

$$Y_c = 967,710 + 1.6026X$$

which may be quite as meaningful to the person habituated to the use of such symbols as is the line of the diagram to those who must have the data in diagrammatic form to be able to "see" the relationship. Whether the line slopes upward or downward to the right, whether the relation is positive or negative, is indicated by the sign of $b$. In our example, $Y$ increases with $X$; hence the value of $b$ is positive. If the relation were negative, the line would slope downward to the right and $b$ would have a minus sign.

## Standard Error of Estimate

The formula for the line of regression puts into mathematical terms only the directionality of the relationship of the bivariate distribution. From the scatter-diagram one obtained an impression

---

[11] In these calculations a larger number of decimals appears than is usual practice. In dealing with large figures the number of decimals to which the intermediate compuations are carried will affect the results considerably.

of the closeness as well as the direction of the relation between the two series; the more closely the points approached the line of regression, the more uniform the relation. The standard error of estimate may be used to describe numerically the closeness of the relationship. It resembles the standard deviation in its conception. It measures the divergence of the various points on the diagram from the line of regression just as the standard deviation measures the dispersion of the various values of a series around their mean. The formula for the standard error of estimate is:

$$S_y = \sqrt{\frac{\Sigma(Y - Y_c)^2}{N}}$$

In this formula the symbol $S_y$ represents the standard error of estimate, or, more specifically, the standard error of estimate of $Y$ from $X$. (As a student browses in the statistics texts he will discover a variety of symbols in use for this measure.) The formula, while formidable in appearance, is only our old friend the standard deviation in another guise and may be readily understood by recalling the nature of that measure. $Y - Y_c$ is the vertical distance from a particular point on the diagram to the line of regression. $Y$ represents the observed, or real, value while $Y_c$ represents its computed value, i.e., if it were calculated from $X$ by the equation of a straight line, and would, therefore, fall on the line of regression. Graphically the deviations from the line of regression (i.e., $Y - Y_c$) appear as in Figure 27.

A simple but laborious method of computing the standard error of estimate is to execute literally the steps specified by the simple formula above, which requires that the value of $Y_c$ be computed for each value of $X$. The New York registration and voting data could, for example, be arranged in columns as follows:

|      | $X$  | $Y$  | $Y_c$   | $Y - Y_c$ | $(Y - Y_c)^2$ |
|------|------|------|---------|-----------|---------------|
| 1924 | 1500 | 3246 | 3371.60 | 125.60    | 15,775.40     |
| 1928 | 2030 | 4406 | 4221.00 | −185.00   | 34,225.00     |
| 1932 | 2340 | 4689 | 4717.71 | 28.71     | 824.26        |

And so on, through the entire series, to obtain from the last column on the right a sum of the squares of the deviations from

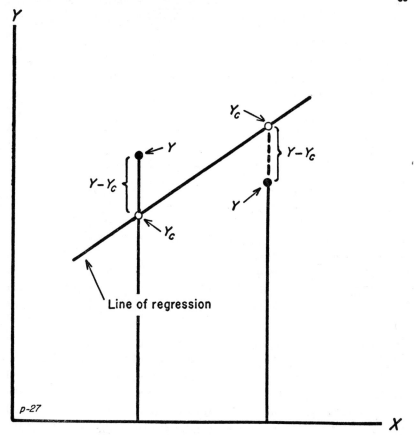

FIGURE 27

*Elements of the Standard Error of Estimate*

the line of regression. The square root of the mean of the squares of the deviations is the standard error of estimate.

The calculation of the values of $Y_c$ may be avoided by the use of the computational formula that follows:

$$S_y = \sqrt{\frac{\Sigma Y^2 - (a\Sigma Y + b\Sigma XY)}{N}}$$

If the values of $a$ and $b$ and the appropriate values from the table on page 80 are substituted, we have:

$$S_y = \sqrt{\frac{201{,}026{,}311 - 967.71(36{,}733) + 1.6026(103{,}188{,}658)}{7}}$$

$$= 124.93$$

If we shift our decimal point back to the units of the original data, we have a standard error of estimate of 124,930 in our particular case. The question is, How much further along are we when we have arrived at this figure? The meaning of the standard error of estimate, when it is used to describe the dispersion of points around the line of regression, is somewhat like the meaning of the standard deviation when it is used to describe the distribution of values around the mean. Lines drawn parallel to the line of regression at a vertical distance of $N$ standard errors of estimate away from the line of regression always bound at a minimum a fixed proportion of the cases. For any bivariate distribution whatsoever, no less than 75% of the cases fall within ±2 standard errors of estimate from the line of regression, and no less than 89% fall within ±3 standard errors of estimate from the line of regression. (In a more or less normal distribution, 68% of the cases will fall within a range of ±1 standard error from the line of regression, 94% within a range of ±1.96 errors.)

In the illustrative case the standard error is 124,930 votes. Two standard errors would be 249,860. The chances are, in accord with the foregoing rule for all distributions, that in at least 75 of 100 instances, the value of $Y$ (the total state turnout) is within plus or minus 249,860 of the computed or estimated state vote.[12] Or, to put the matter differently, the chances are that in at least 75 of 100 instances the actual values of $Y$ fall within plus or minus 249,860 of the line of regression. In fact, in this instance four of the seven instances fall within plus or minus one standard error of estimate, almost meeting the expectation for a normal distribution, and all the points are within plus or minus two standard errors of estimate.

The fact that registration precedes voting may suggest the possibility of using the line of regression as an instrument of predic-

[12] As has doubtless been deduced by now the standard error of estimate is so named because it may be used as a measure of the range of error in estimating $Y$ from $X$.

tion. A word of warning is in order. The predictive quality of a line of regression (and its standard error of estimate) depends on the assumption that the relationships described will continue to prevail, that is, upon the assumption that the next case added will not alter the direction of the line. All the line does is to define the past direction; it does not probe into the future. Undoubtedly for many purposes the stability of relations is such that $Y$ may be predicted from $X$, but the art of prediction comes in the capacity to foresee alterations in past uniformity and not in the ability to chart persistence.

## *The Line of Regression, the Standard Error, and Trends in Series*

An interpolation becomes in order at this point to indicate a special application of the techniques just explained. At an earlier point (pages 34–36) the problem of analyzing and measuring long-term, or secular, trends was mentioned. Also, the discussion of the measurement of the fluctuations of time series pointed out that the standard deviation was inappropriate as a measure of short-term variations of a series undergoing a secular trend. The line of regression may be used to describe a secular trend and the standard error of estimate may be used to measure short-term fluctuations about that trend.

The graph in Panel A of Figure 28, which shows the Democratic percentage of the vote for governor in Franklin County, Massachusetts, illustrates the problem. Short-term fluctuations in Democratic strength occurred in this county from 1920 to 1948, but they occurred around a rising secular trend of Democratic strength. If one wishes to measure the short-term fluctuations, a means must be found to separate them from the secular trend. The line of regression provides both a description of the secular trend and a base from which to measure the short-term fluctuations in the series.

To fit a line to a secular trend that appears to be linear, one treats the years or other time periods included in the time series as the $X$ variate, and the percentage of vote (if one is working with this type of series) as the $Y$ variate. To simplify computation, one substitutes consecutive numbers from 0 through $N$ for the ac-

tual years or other time intervals of the series. For example, if
the series includes the thirteen presidential elections from 1900
to 1948, the numbers 0 to 12 may be substituted as the $X$ variate.
The line of regression, when computed, shows the secular trend.[13]

Panel A of Figure 28 illustrates the use of the line of regression
to describe a secular trend and to provide a base from which to
measure short-term fluctuations around a long-term trend. The
line of regression, which slopes upward, suggests that during the
period 1920–1948 this non-metropolitan Massachusetts county
was undergoing a gradual, long-term political change. Yet throughout this period short-term fluctuations occurred in Democratic
strength, just as they did in jurisdictions marked by a more stable
division of party strength. The supposition is that one may separate out and measure these short-term fluctuations by calculating
their dispersion around the line of regression. The standard error
of estimate measures that dispersion. In this instance the standard
error of estimate amounts to 3.7 per cent, which constitutes a
measure of short-term variation around the ascending secular trend. (The equation for the trend line in Panel A is
$Y = 21.5 + 1.33X$, with origin at 1920 and $X$ as two years, the
interval between elections. Later in the chapter we shall return
to Panels B and C in Figure 28.)

In Panel A lines appear at a vertical distance of 2 standard
errors of estimate above and below the line of regression. The
proportion of the items of a time series that may be expected to
fall within plus or minus 1 or 2 standard errors of estimate is not
that which prevails for a normal distribution. For a bivariate
distribution to be normal both the $X$ and $Y$ variates must each be
normally distributed by themselves. These conditions automati-
cally exclude from this type of distribution those in which, as in
this instance, one aspect of the distribution consists of equal time
intervals. In a series such as this, the $X$ variate, that is, the frequency of elections, can never be distributed normally. Such a
distribution must always be rectangular with a frequency of 1

---

[13] Computation from the midpoint of the series considerably simplifies matters,
especially if the series includes many items. The procedure may be found described
in any elementary statistics text.

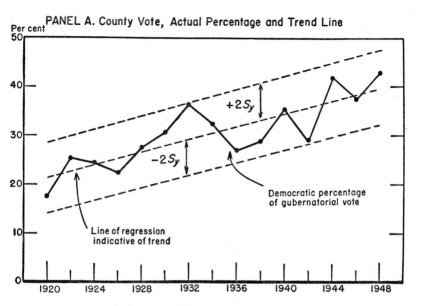

PANEL A. County Vote, Actual Percentage and Trend Line

+2S_y

−2S_y

Democratic percentage
of gubernatorial vote

Line of regression
indicative of trend

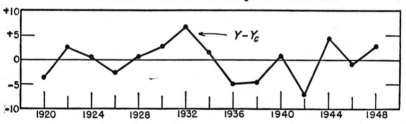

PANEL B. Deviation of Actual Percentage from Trend Line

$Y - Y_c$

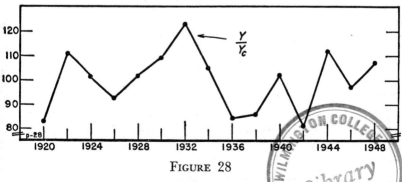

PANEL C. Actual as Percentage of Line of Regression

$\dfrac{Y}{Y_c}$

FIGURE 28

*Democratic Percentage of Two-Party Vote for Governor, Franklin
County, Massachusetts, 1920–1948*

for each value of X. Although in this case all the items fall within
plus or minus 2 standard errors of estimate, the generally applicable rule would require an expectation of not less than 75 per
cent of the items within that range.

### Another Example of the Use of the Standard Error of Estimate

After the detour to explain the fitting of a line to a secular
trend, let us return to the main argument. The ultimate aim of
that argument was to show how the visual impression from a
scatter-diagram of a relation between two time series could be
measured or converted into precise terms. In the case of the New
York City registration and the total state vote the relationship
of the two variables appeared to be quite close. Another example,
without so uniform a relationship, will aid the exposition.

In Figure 29 a pair of graphs appear representing the Democratic percentage of the gubernatorial vote in Maine and the Dem-

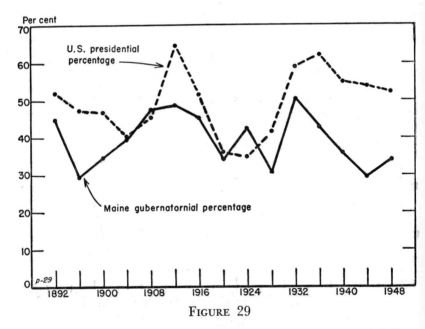

FIGURE 29

*Democratic Percentage of Two-Party Maine Gubernatorial Vote
and of Two-Party United States Presidential Vote, 1892–1948*

ocratic percentage of the presidential vote in the United States over the period 1892–1948. The two graphs appear to move generally in the same direction, or at least so it seems from a casual inspection. The parallelism of movement has had a special attractiveness in that Maine's custom of holding its gubernatorial elections in September gave rise, during the long lean days of the Democrats, to the saying that, as Maine goes, so goes the nation, viz., Republican. In later days it has been suggested that the

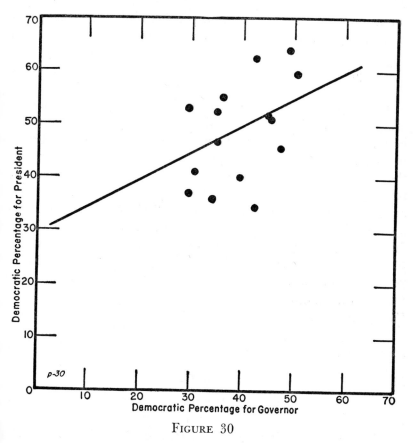

FIGURE 30

*Scatter-Diagram of Relationship between Democratic Percentage of Two-Party Maine Gubernatorial Vote and Two-Party United States Presidential Vote, 1892–1948*

Democratic proportion of the September vote in Maine might provide a clue to what the Democratic proportion of the vote in the nation would be in November.

Before placing any substantial wager that a particular Democratic percentage in the Maine gubernatorial vote in September will be followed by a particular Democratic percentage in the nation in November, the prudent man will seek to determine the closeness or uniformity of the relation between the two series. The scatter-diagram, the line of regression, and the standard error of estimate, as we have seen, provide tools for making this estimate. The data of the graphs of Figure 29 are plotted on a scatter-diagram in Figure 30. The line of regression for the data ($Y_c = 29.7 + .501X$) also appears on the diagram as an upward sloping line.

The points are seen to be widely scattered about the line of regression. The slope of the line of regression indicates that there is some positive relationship between Maine's gubernatorial vote in September and the nation's presidential vote in November, but the wide dispersion of the points about the line indicates that the relationship is of low degree. The standard error of estimate amounts to 7.985 per cent. If we applied the rule stated earlier, a prediction would be expected to have 75 chances out of 100 of falling within a range of $\pm 2$ standard errors of the actual value of Y. In this instance this would mean within a range of $\pm 15.97$ per cent of the national vote, or a total range of 31.94 per cent. One would eventually achieve bankruptcy, if he persisted in the folly of interpreting the September Maine vote as a straw in the national wind unless a drastic change occurred in the established relationships.

## Measuring Relative Closeness of Fit

The standard error of estimate provides a measure of the closeness of the points of a particular distribution to the line of regression. Or, to put it in another way, the standard error of estimate measures the dispersion of the points around the line of regression. However, it measures dispersion in the absolute numbers used in the calculation. The standard error of estimate in the New York case, 124,930, is meaningful only in relation to the particular line of regression. Similarly, in the Maine case the standard error of estimate was 7.985 per cent. Again, this is meaningful only in relation to the changing values of $Y$ on the line of regression in the particular case.

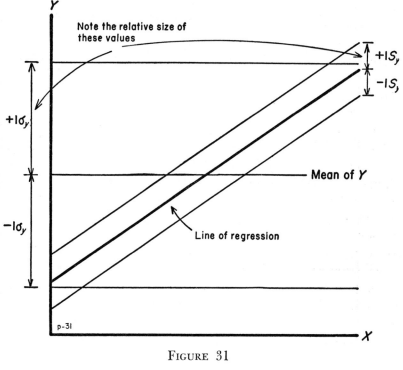

FIGURE 31

*A "High" Correlation*

Obviously it would be useful to process the figures in some way so that we could describe the closeness of the relationship in relative terms, that is, in a form that would permit comparisons of the closeness of different distributions around the line of regression whatever their absolute values might be. Can we say, for example, that a set of points in one scatter-diagram clusters more closely about its line of regression than another set in another diagram? In the case of the standard deviation a coefficient of variation can be used to indicate the degree of dispersion around the mean value. That coefficient is simply standard deviation as a percentage of the mean, a single value. In the present problem the values of $Y$ are dispersed around the line of regression, itself a changing value, and no such simple ratio as the coefficient of variation will serve our purpose.

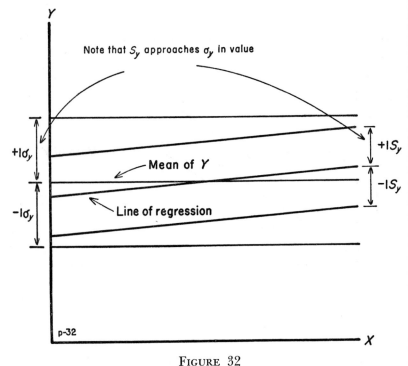

FIGURE 32

*A "Low" Correlation*

The solution of the problem may be suggested by close examination of Figures 31 and 32. Figure 31 represents a high correlation on the order of that built on the New York data. In this figure the points on the diagram would be clustered closely around and along the line of regression. On the other hand the $Y$ values represented by the points would be widely dispersed around the mean of $Y$. The value of $X$, in the New York case the registration figure, would be much more closely related to the value of $Y_o$ than would the mean of the $Y$ values.

Figure 32, in contrast, represents the type of distribution involved in the Maine data. The points would be dispersed almost as widely around the line of regression as around the mean of the $Y$ values. The fit would not be close. From a given value of $X$ one would know little more about the corresponding value of $Y$ than if he attempted to estimate that value from the mean of $Y$. It should be observed that the differences between the two figures do not depend on the differences in the slope of the line of regression.

The relationship shown in Figures 31 and 32 provides the elements for a ratio by which the closeness of fit to the line of regression may be measured. As the standard error of estimate of $Y$ approaches in size the standard deviation of $Y$, the distribution becomes relatively more widely dispersed around the line of regression, that is, the degree of relationship between the $X$ and $Y$ values declines. On the other hand, as the standard estimate of error of $Y$ declines in size in relation to the standard deviation of $Y$ (represented by the symbol for the standard deviation with a subscript, $\sigma_y$), the higher is the degree of relation prevailing between the values of $X$ and $Y$.

A measure of the closeness of relationship between $X$ and $Y$ thus may be:

$$\frac{S_y}{\sigma_y}$$

In our earlier problem on New York City registration and the New York state vote this ratio is:

$$\frac{124{,}930}{1{,}086{,}750} = 0.115$$

The Maine gubernatorial and the national presidential data can be put in the form of the same ratio:

$$\frac{7.985}{8.66} = .922$$

The Maine data scattered widely around the line of regression; the lack of closeness of fit was obvious; the ratio of 0.92 approaches 1 and indicates that the standard error of estimate is almost as great as the standard deviation of the $Y$ values. The New York ratio of 0.115 indicates the contrary state of affairs, viz., that the standard error of estimate of $Y$ is quite small in relation to the standard deviation and that the points are clustered closely about the line of regression.

One drawback of the ratio is that it increases in value as the relation we want to measure declines in closeness or as the points become more widely dispersed about the line of regression. Or the ratio declines in value as the closeness of the relation between $X$ and $Y$ increases. The ratio also has more serious disadvantages in that it lacks certain mathematical properties of the conventional coefficient of correlation; those properties will become apparent in the next chapter. Let it be said that statisticians are horrified by the ratio and that it is only introduced here as one step in an effort to convey some glimmer of an understanding of the procedure.

The ratio conventionally used, the Pearsonian coefficient of correlation, represented by the symbol $r$, converts the above ratio into a coefficient that increases in value, toward a maximum of 1, as the closeness of the relation increases. As this coefficient approaches 0, the closeness of the relation declines. Its formula is:

$$r = \sqrt{1 - \frac{S_y{}^2}{\sigma_y{}^2}}$$

Substituting the Maine data in this formula, we obtain:

$$r = \sqrt{1 - \frac{7.985^2}{8.66^2}} = +0.387$$

The plus sign (which is derived from the sign of $b$ in the regression equation) indicates that the relationship is positive, that $Y$ increases with $X$ or that the line of regression slopes upwards. The size of the coefficient indicates a low degree of relationship. On the other hand, $r$ for the New York data is $+0.99$, which approaches the highest possible degree of correlation, 1.0. The coefficient tells us the closeness of the relationship and the direction, positive or negative, of the line of regression, but it provides no information about the slope of the line.[14] Hence it is ordinarily considered good practice, in reporting a correlation analysis, to indicate the value of $Y_c$ as well as the coefficient of correlation.[15]

## Questions about the Correlation of Time Series: Secular and Short-Term Components of Time Series

The examples in the correlation of time series represent applications of the technique to a particular type of data and to a special type of problem. Certain basic questions in the correlation of time series need to be set out and their bearing on the interpretation of the examples needs to be emphasized. The statistical handbooks often admonish their readers not to correlate time series in their raw form. The reasons for this rest in part on the nature of the correlation procedure and in part on the fact that many procedures for the analysis of time series have been designed so as to be adapted to the problems and data of economics. The wealth of time series available to the economic analyst permits types of studies that the political scientist could scarcely attempt for lack of data. Moreover, the nature of economic series—

[14] The student should be warned that the procedure outlined to explain the coefficient of correlation is too laborious for general use. A computational formula will be set out in the next chapter.

[15] A short cut in the computation of the standard error of estimate may be useful to remember. When a coefficient of correlation is computed, values are usually produced or can easily be produced (depending on the formula employed) from which the standard error of estimate may be derived by substitution in the following formula:

$$S_y = \sigma_y \sqrt{1 - r^2}$$

Thus, in the Maine instance:

$$S_y = 8.66\sqrt{1 - 0.387^2}$$
$$= 0.7985$$

with measurements at monthly, weekly, even daily intervals— encourage the contrivance of techniques often not usefully applicable to the political series commonly available.

The more basic problem in the application of correlation analysis comes from the fact that time series may be made up of several components. Suppose a series on the annual output of passenger automobiles in the United States since 1910. It would show a secular or long-term upward movement. Along the upward trend line would appear minor departures from the path of secular movement. Some of these would appear as periodicities that reflected the effects of the business cycle. Other irregularities would also appear in the curve for various more or less unique or accidental reasons, such as wartime curtailment of production.

The economic analyst needs to separate these various components of a time series, for each represents a special type of economic behavior and presents its own problems of analysis. The secular or trend component of a series may be defined or extracted by fitting a straight line or an appropriate curve to a series. The procedure may, in some instances, be the same as that followed in fitting a line to the series on the Democratic percentage of the gubernatorial vote in Franklin County, Massachusetts, in Figure 28 on page 87. The straight line in that figure could be taken as representing a secular trend around which election-to-election fluctuations occurred in response to the circumstances of each campaign.

Periodicities may also be segregated out of a series for analysis. If one is studying cyclical questions, for example, he needs to sift out that part of the variation in the series attributable to the long-term trend. One method of doing this may be illustrated by again referring to Figure 28 on page 87. By obtaining the value of $Y_c$ for each election year one can determine the deviation of the actual vote from the line of regression or the secular trend. Then a graph showing these deviations above and below a horizontal line delineates the short-term fluctuations of the vote with the trend removed. These operations underlie Panel B of Figure 28. In that panel the graph flutters nicely above and below a horizontal line unencumbered by the secular trend as do the financial-page graphs of economic series that have been subjected to some such process, usually of a more complex nature.

Obviously it is useful to be able to segregate components of a time series that have an apparent separateness in the phenomenon covered by the series. Beyond this—and here we begin to get to the relevance of all this for our problem—if one wishes to study certain types of relationships by correlation, the nature of correlation procedure is such that the time series must be broken into its component parts. Any two secular trends moving in the same direction are apt to show a relatively high correlation even though their periodicities are negatively correlated or scarcely related at all. Thus a secular upward movement in the production of beans since 1900 would probably be associated with a secular upward movement in the price of beans. Along the secular production trend more or less periodic fluctuations in output would probably occur. Along the price trend similar periodicities would occur. Correlation of the two trends in their raw form would result in a positive correlation because of their more or less parallel secular movement. If the problem is to determine the relation between the price and production of beans, some way has to be contrived to wash out the secular or trend component, for it would be supposed that the minor fluctuations of price would rise when the minor fluctuations of supply dropped below the trend line. By fitting an appropriate curve or line to the production trend one can abstract the short-term deviations from the trend by some such technique as that alluded to in the mention of Figure 28. The trend in the real price series might be removed by the use of an appropriate price index. (Illustrative is the similar operation performed in Panel C of Figure 28 where the actual percentages were divided by the values of $Y_c$ or the trend line which was treated, in effect, as an index.) The removal of that trend would result in two series that measured short-term fluctuations in price and production independently of the secular components of the series. These two series would probably show a negative correlation with production declines associated with

price rises and vice versa. That relation between price and production fluctuations would not be revealed by the correlation of
the raw series.

Technique, thus, must be adapted to the problem to which it
is to be applied. In the case of the New York data on registration
in the city and voting in the state (Figure 25, page 75) both
series are characterized by a secular upward trend, although it is
evident that minor variations also occur in the series. Each curve,
however, bundles up together secular and short-term factors. The
problem was to estimate the relation between total city registration and total state turnout a short time later in the year. Since
the largest element of each of the series appeared to be the component of secular growth, to relate the absolute size of city registration to that of the state vote, separation of the secular and short-
term components of the series would have been out of order. The
closeness of the relation between the two series rested fundamentally on their common association with the growth of the electorate. Once the two curves flatten out, a simple ratio between
them would probably be suitable for the purpose of projection
from the registration to the vote.

If certain other sorts of problems were being attacked, the
secular and short-term elements of the New York series would have
to be separated. Thus if the desire were to determine whether the
voters of the city were more responsive to the excitements of campaigns (as measured by voting turnout) than were the upstate citizens, the trends would have to be removed from the series. This
could be done, for example, by converting the absolute vote of
each series into a percentage of the estimated citizen populations
21 and over. Even these series might show trends in participation
rates that would have to be removed to obtain in a more or less
pure form the fluctuations attributable to the influences imping-
ing on the voter from campaign to campaign. The two series then
could be correlated to measure the degree of similarity of short-
term variations in the series from which the trend had been removed.

The Maine case presented a situation in some respects similar
to the New York problem but in other respects dissimilar. The

problem was to estimate the utility, on the basis of past performance, of the Democratic percentage of the Maine two-party gubernatorial vote in September as an indicator of the Democratic percentage of the national two-party presidential vote in November. Both series recorded in Figure 29 (page 88) contain a long-term trend, at least in the sense that a line fitted by the method of least squares would slope slightly upward in the case of the presidential series ($Y = 45.7 + .535X$, with origin at 1892 and $X$ as four years) and slightly downward for the gubernatorial series ($Y = 42.2 - .4X$, with origin at 1892 and $X$ as four years). The two Maine series also contained a component of short-term fluctuations more or less cyclical in nature. Both the cyclical and secular aspects of the series affect the closeness of the September Maine vote division to the November national division. The coefficient of correlation, as it was computed, took both elements into account for that reason.

If in the case of the Maine problem the concern were with a comparison of the amplitude and direction of short-term fluctuations in Democratic strength in Maine and the United States, the secular trends should be removed from the two series if an exact measure were required. That could be done by fitting lines by the method of least squares to the Maine and United States series. One means of removing the trend values from each item of the series is to treat the value of $Y_c$ at each point in time as an index number. The real value of $Y$ is converted into a percentage of the corresponding $Y_c$. Thus the items in the series above the line of regression turn out to be above 100 in value and those below it to be less than 100, as in Panel C of Figure 28 on page 87. The application of this procedure to the Maine data yields a coefficient of correlation of $+0.45$ in contrast with that of $+0.387$ obtained without elimination of the trend from the series. As was apparent from inspection of the graphs, the secular factors were responsible in part for the low degree of association between the Maine and national votes.

Since many electoral time series consist of comparatively short series of items taken at two- or four-year intervals, the legitimacy of fitting lines or curves to them may often be doubtful. An apparent trend may be a reflection of the peculiar accidents of an election or two rather than a manifestation of a genuine trend gradually and continuously operative over a long period of time. Whatever trend appears may well simply be a function of the mathematical procedure rather than an indication of the nature of the underlying human behavior. The truth of the matter is that practically no effort has been made to test the utility of systematic methods for the analysis of the time series in the study of electoral series. Furthermore, these methods might turn out to be of special utility in the study of financial series and other data on administrative operations of concern to the political scientist.

### 3. The Uses of Time Series

The explanation of quantitative techniques tends, perhaps by exhaustion, to distract attention from the types of questions to which one applies them. The books on pedagogy suggest teaching by citation of example. Yet in that process the general idea may be blotted out by the ubiquity of the particular. Lest it be supposed that the particular uses outlined in the preceding pages encompass all the possibilities, a few words by way of general conclusion may be in order.

In purely formal terms the analysis of paired time series involves the determination of the relationships between the fluctuations of two variables through time. That relation may be uniformly negative or positive in varying degree. In some instances special analytical significance attaches to particular deviations from an otherwise uniform pattern of relationships.[16] In another category of applications, exemplified by the German-American cases, the paired series measure the behavior through time of two unlike entities whose response to particular events, stimuli,

---

[16] The attribution of significance to individual deviations implicitly involves the determination of the interrelation between three or more series. Two series may vary together over a long period of time but a single exception occurs. In that instance "other things" did not remain "equal." A third series, which in some cases may be quantified, may be supposed to have been operative all along but at the point of deviation the aberrations of the third series upset the "normal" relation between the two under observation.

or factors is to be compared. To these broad categories might be added some of the types of inference from single series described in the preceding chapter.

The foregoing categorization relates only to the forms of analysis, which may be of varying degrees of intricacy. The more significant aspect of the matter relates to the kind of substantive questions that may be coped with by putting time series through such mechanical processes. The fact that the data of time series happen to be in quantitative form should not be permitted to conceal the fact that the basic analytical operation employed in their examination does not differ from that often followed in the interpretation of unquantified data.

The essential logical operation in the analysis of paired time series is the comparative method applied to a sequence of cases spread through time rather than to a number of situations each contemporary or simultaneous with the other. The basic objective in either instance is to determine functional relations: Whether A is associated with B, or whether when A happens so does B. Such an objective may be pursued by the observation of a large number of contemporaneous or simultaneous instances and the interpretation of the findings fundamentally by Mill's method of agreement or by the method of difference or by both. It is possible, however, also to regard a pair of time series as a number of instances and, as has been argued, to interpret the observed relations in the same manner.

In the comparison of contemporary and different instances, other things, save the variable whose significance is in question, are rarely equal. The problem of analysis is thereby complicated. For some purposes and for some types of questions the comparison of items in a time series simplifies matters, for "other things" may be more nearly "equal." For example, for some purposes a comparison of a series of elections within a New Hampshire town may be more illuminating, or at least less confused by imponderables, than a comparison of an election in a New Hampshire town and another in a French commune. "Other things" may be more nearly "equal," although the historical dimension has a way of introducing its own disturbing factors for which the analyst must be alert.[17]

By such general methods of reasoning one may interpret the relations found to exist between two series. If two series concerning the same jurisdiction or object of study fluctuate together uniformly, one may have some support for the supposition that they are causally related. By the same token, it is possible to compare time series relating to different objects of study (jurisdictions, etc.) in order to test hunches about causal relations or, better, association. If different types of units respond differently to a common variable or circumstance, the significance of their differential response may be better appraised. The student should remember that the fact that B follows A, or that B occurs with A, proves nothing. Some hidden or unseen variable may be at the bottom of it all. On the other hand, no other means exists to exclude the unrelated or to underpin our plausible hunches; in any case, too much attention to epistemology induces hallucinations of negativism.

Apart from the testing of hypotheses about causal relations or associations, the analysis of time series permits systematic treatment of questions of concurrent variations that are of common origin or that describe different aspects of the same phenomenon. In the description of intricate political institutions or practices paired series have considerable utility.

The formulation of such general categories of questions that may be attacked by the analysis of paired time series may not be very helpful in the acquisition of skill in application. A tortuous and often painful intellectual process tends to be involved as one contrives ways and means for testing the validity of particular hypotheses or hunches. Skill seems to come only from long practice although native ingenuity may help. In the application of the techniques outlined in this chapter one may need to rely less on

[17] In the study of time series the question must be kept in mind whether the series records a sequence of more or less separate events or whether the points on the graph are readings at particular moments of a phenomenon with a continuing existence through time. What is the connection in nature, so to speak, between the points that we connect with a line on a graph? Failure to raise this question may lead to serious errors of interpretation.

"flashes of insight," if he explicitly asks such questions as whether the "circumstances," "event," or "situation" with which he deals is one of a series, whether other series are available that might bear on the primary series, whether a comparison may be usefully had from a like series relating to another jurisdiction, whether the possibility of deviation from or conformity to a time series pattern would be illuminating. Even when the analytical procedure is made explicit by the deliberate raising of such questions, imagination and ingenuity must play no mean role in the formulation of operating research procedures.

**References**

*Method*

M. R. Cohen and E. Nagel, *An Introduction to Logic and Scientific Method* (Harcourt, Brace, and Co., 1934), chaps. 11, 12, 13. Chapter 13 consists of an exposition and critique of Mill's formulation of the methods of experimental inquiry.

F. E. Croxton and D. J. Cowden, *Applied General Statistics* (Prentice-Hall, 1939), Chap. 25, "Correlation of Time Series and Forecasting."

Alfred de Grazia, "The Process of Theory-Research Interaction," *Journal of Politics,* 13 (1951), pp. 88–99.

S. J. Eldersveld, "Theory and Method of Voting Behavior Research," *Journal of Politics,* 13 (1951), pp. 70–87.

J. S. Mill, *A System of Logic* (eighth ed.), bk. III, chaps. 8, 9.

F. C. Mills, *Statistical Methods* (Holt, rev. ed., 1938), Chap. 11, "The Measurement of Relationship between Time Series."

Karl Pearson, *The Grammar of Science* (London: Everyman Ed., 1937), Chap. 3, "The Scientific Law."

*Applications*

Johan Akerman, "Political Economic Cycles," *Kyklos, International Review for Social Sciences,* 1 (1947), pp. 107–117.

L. H. Bean, *How to Predict Elections* (Knopf, 1948), Chap. 6, "When Business Cycle Meets Political Cycle."

W. C. Clark, *Economic Aspects of a President's Popularity* (Philadelphia, 1943).

Samuel Lubell, *The Future of American Politics* (Harper, 1952).

S. S. Nilson, *Histoire et Sciences Politiques* (Bergen: Chr. Michelsen Institute, 1950). Contains citations and summary of many relevant studies.

W. F. Ogburn and A. J. Jaffe, "Business Conditions in Presidential Election Years," *American Political Science Review,* 30 (1936), pp. 269–275.

F. A. Pearson and W. I. Myers, "Prices and Presidents," *Farm Economics* (New York State College of Agriculture), No. 163, September, 1948, pp. 4210–4218.

M. S. Stedman, Jr., and S. W. Stedman, *Discontent at the Polls, A Study of Farmer and Labor Parties, 1827–1948* (New York: Columbia University Press, 1950).

Clark Tibbitts, "Majority Votes and the Business Cycle," *American Journal of Sociology,* 36 (1931), pp. 596–606.

Thomas Wilkinson and Hornell Hart, "Prosperity and Political Victory," *Public Opinion Quarterly,* 14 (1950), pp. 331–335.

R. C. White, "Prosperity and Political Parties," *Social Forces,* 6 (1927), pp. 105–111.

Dale Yoder, "Economic Changes and Industrial Unrest in the United States," *Journal of Political Economy,* 48 (1940) pp. 222–237.

# 4

## SIMPLE CORRELATION

The preceding chapter centered on the problem of ascertaining the relationships between two factors through time. Here the main concern revolves around the ascertainment of the relationship between two variables occurring in a number of "instances" or situations at one point in time. The technical procedures—the formulae—for processing both types of data are the same. Some repetition in explanation of mathematical procedures will occur; but since even the simplest statistical conceptions are difficult to grasp, perhaps pedagogical expediency justifies repetition.

The logic underlying the process of correlation amounts in essence to a special application of Mill's canon of concomitant variations. Perhaps we may best explain that canon by cheerfully conceding that in the preceding chapters we played fast and loose with Mr. Mill's methods. He called his first canons—the method of difference, the method of agreement, and the joint method of agreement and difference—"methods of experimental inquiry." They were evidently designed largely to deal with problems such as: Vaccinate A against smallpox; give B an injection of distilled water; expose A and B to smallpox; A survives; B does not; Q.E.D. When one uses methods designed for the analysis of invariant relations to reason about changes of degree in aggregates, e.g., groups such as the electorate of Comal County, Texas, there are evident hazards. Mill set out the method of concomitant variations to cope with phenomena in which changes were of degree rather than dichotomous as in the smallpox case. He stated his canon: "Whatever phenomenon varies in any manner whenever another phenomenon varies in some particular manner, is either a cause or an effect of that phenomenon, or is connected with it through some fact of causation."

Thus the length of a steel rail could probably be shown to vary, according to some formula, with its temperature. Or the variation in production of corn on different plots of irrigated land could be shown to bear a relationship to the quantities of water applied. The statistical procedure of correlation, in some applications at least, is simply a method of measuring these concomitant variations. The extension of the method of correlation to those phenomena to which political scientists often apply it may involve some violence to the formal, logical method. We ascertain, say, the relation between the Democratic percentage of the vote by counties in a particular state in 1928 and the Catholic percentage of church membership. Whether Democratic percentage–Catholic percentage, as characteristics of the county, are comparable with temperature-length, as characteristics of the steel rail, may be questioned. Nevertheless, the technique of correlation provides a ready and easy way of determining the relation, if any, between two sets of variable characteristics of "instances," "phenomena," "circumstances," "situations."

It does not follow that the identification of concomitant variations necessarily unearths causal relations. Generations of jibers at statisticians have pointed out that a high degree of correlation prevails between the monthly rainfall in Philadelphia and in Trenton, but that rain in Trenton does not cause rain in Independence Square or *vice versa*. The statisticians thought of this one before the jibers did. Mill covered himself against this sort of attack by saying that jointly varying phenomena, if not causally related, might be connected "through some fact of causation." Even so, in the absence of an experimental technique to control the variables entering into a given set of situations, it is better to speak of relationship or association than of cause. And, in the analysis of recorded political data, even the most plausible sort of correlation may become implausible when field inquiry supplements work with the calculator.

The discussion of correlation in the preceding chapter centered mainly on the "closeness" of the relation between two variables. The same sorts of data and the same mathematical procedures may be thrown into another perspective and used to think about another broad sort of question, a special case of the analysis of concomitant variations. That question, which differs in verbal emphasis if not in its mathematical nature from the question of "closeness" or degree of relationship, is essentially the determination of what proportion of the variation in the dependent variable can be attributed to variation in the independent variable.[1] The independent variable, as the term implies, is the variable whose changes cause variation in the other, or dependent, variable. Thus, variation in heat or temperature is an independent variable causing variation in length of the rail.

Even the experimental sciences have their difficulties. Consider our case of the plots to which varying quantities of water are applied. Despite the best efforts the plots will vary slightly in fertility, in the manner of their cultivation, or in other factors affecting corn production. The points plotting production and water used would be somewhat scattered around the line of best fit, be it linear or non-linear. The production would vary from plot to plot, but the variations would be influenced, at least to some extent, by other factors as well as by variations in the quantity of water. What part of the variation from plot to plot in corn production could be accounted for in terms of variations in $X$, the quantity of water applied? An answer of sorts to such questions may be obtained by utilizing the data of a scatter-diagram and computing the coefficient of determination. Although not so widely used as the conventional coefficient of correlation, this measure has advantages in dealing with some types of political data.

---

[1] Variance, in statistical usage, has a meaning different from the everyday English word, variation, but variation will serve for the moment in this discussion.

## 1. The Coefficient of Determination

The student who has been struggling to follow the argument will pull us up short at this point and inquire whither the discussion is leading. The chapter began with mention of the canon of concomitant variations, leapt to the question of what part of the variation in the dependent variable could be attributed to variation in the independent variable, and from thence went to the coefficient of determination. The explanation of detailed techniques should be simpler if their broad purpose or general idea is clearly understood. For many persons knowledge of statistics need not go beyond the broad concepts to the details of computation; for those who use the detailed techniques a comprehension of the general idea is indispensable.

### The Idea of Concomitant Variation

Perhaps it would be helpful to backtrack and to make explicit what must be apparent by now, viz., that many statistical procedures rest on an assumption that the world is not black and white but is made up of many shades of gray. Variables, such as shades of gray, may be represented by numbers. Description becomes a task of indicating numerically differences of degree rather than of categorization. Numbers indicating differences of degree may be grouped in frequency distributions and may be described by frequency curves, by measures of central tendency, by measures of dispersion, and in other ways. Whether one works with quantitative techniques or otherwise, the basic notion of differences of degree is commonplace. The most casual observer may quickly conclude that the categories of Democrat and Republican serve illy, for they conceal a distribution over a continuum; a statistically oriented person might set about to contrive attitude scales along which Republicans and Democrats could be ranked in accord with their differences of degree.

Now comes a step that may be a bit abstruse. In the categorical world of invariant relations it may be said that B follows A or is associated with A. In the statistical world of variables, in contrast with attributes, it may be said that a change of degree in B follows or is associated with a change of degree in **A**. The nature of such an association between changes of degree in A and B may be shown graphically in a scatter-diagram. Characteristics of the association may be measured by the line of regression, the standard error of estimate, and the coefficient of correlation.

In some instances the associated changes in degree of two variables fit a mathematical description in which $Y$ is said to be a function of $X$. Such a relationship need not be the simple instance of an association of a 10 per cent increase in one variable with a 10 per cent increase in the other. The relation may be more complex; the associations between pairs of differences of degree may themselves be of varying degree. Thus if all the points on a scatter-diagram fall on a straight line, the functional relationship between the two variables would be expressed by the equation for a straight line, $Y = a + bX$. (A little reflection will indicate that even that simple relationship need not be a matter of a 10 per cent change being associated with a 10 per cent change.) Or if all the points on the diagram fall on a curve, the functional relationship could be expressed by the equation for whatever sort of curve was involved.

## Measurement of Associated Variations

If all the points on a scatter-diagram regularly fell on a line, straight or curved, the perfect functional relationship between the two variables could be described by the appropriate equation and that would be the end of the problem. In fact, that condition infrequently occurs; it is only approximated. Third variables and inaccuracies of observation intrude to cause deviations from the line apparently describing the "true" underlying relation between two variables. Hence, the problem arises of measuring the proportion of the variation in one series that is associated with or explained by the variation in a series with which it is paired. The coefficient of determination provides such a measure. The problem is to build up its formula so as to explain both its mathematics and its meaning in relation to our basic problem of method. Since the coefficient of correlation is the square root of the coefficient of determination, the exposition will, perhaps fortunately, traverse some familiar ground. At the outset it is essential to emphasize a statistical concept that is related to the measures of dispersion discussed in the preceding pages: the concept of *total variance* or simply *variance*. Variance is the square of the standard deviation; or, it is the mean of the squares of the deviations from the mean, the figure one gets before he extracts the square root to arrive at the standard deviation. Variance is thus a measure of dispersion or, to use our earlier figure, a measure of the differences in degree among the items in a frequency distribution.

A companion measure may be called the *error variance,* although terminological usage is not uniform. The error variance is the square of the standard error of estimate or the mean of the squares of the deviations from the line of regression. It is thus a measure of dispersion around the line of regression. The coefficient of determination is a relationship that involves as its principal components the variance and the error variance of the *Y* variate of a bivariate distribution.

Let us keep firmly in mind the notions of variance and error variance and attend to the bivariate distribution in Figure 33. The points in the diagram are dispersed around their mean, indicated on the chart as $\overline{Y}$. They are also dispersed around their line of regression. The deviations from $\overline{Y}$ are indicated by broken lines; those from the line of regression by solid lines.

The values of *Y* in Figure 33 might be assumed to represent the rate of corn production on different plots of irrigated land, the values of *X*, to represent the quantities of water applied. If a linear relationship is supposed to exist, some factor or factors other than quantity of water evidently also affected production. Production varies around the mean of *Y*, by the amounts represented by the dotted lines. Production also varies around the line of regression by the values represented by the unbroken lines. To discover the significance of variations in irrigation, one must attempt to determine what proportion of the variation of production around $\overline{Y}$ is associated with or accounted for by the degree to which the values of *Y* tend to cluster around the line of regression. The problem becomes in essence one of measuring the relation between the broken and unbroken lines, or, more technically, their squares.

Consider first the ratio of the error variance to the total variance. The numerator of this ratio would be the mean of the squares of the solid vertical lines in Figure 33, which represent the deviations from the line of regression. The denominator of the ratio would be the mean of the squares of the broken lines, which represent the deviations from the mean of the $Y$ values.

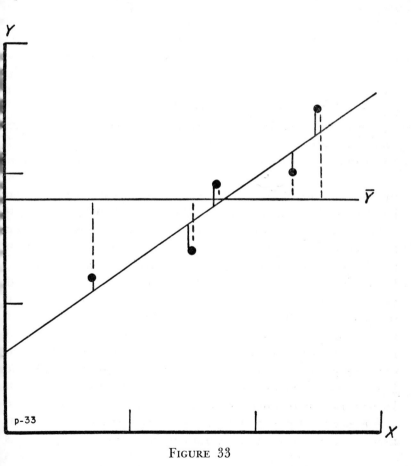

FIGURE 33

*Elements of the Coefficient of Determination*

The broken lines in Figure 33 are seen to be longer on the average than the solid lines. A considerable proportion of variation in output is associated with variations in water input. If all the points fell on the line of regression, the solid lines would disappear. Then the mean square of the deviations from the line of regression would become 0. The ratio between the mean square of the two sets of deviations would then be 0. All the variation in output among our plots would be accounted for by variations in water input. When the points are widely dispersed about the line of regression, the solid lines approach in length the broken lines. If the mean square of the deviations from the line of regression equaled the mean square of the deviations from the mean of $Y$, the resulting ratio would then be equal to 1. Under those circumstances none of the variance in corn output would be associated with the variation in water input.

The mean square of deviations from the line of regression cannot exceed the mean square of the deviations from the mean of $Y$, a proposition that will have to be taken on faith here. Hence, the ratio between these two squares can never exceed 1. Since both the numerator and denominator of the ratio are squares and cannot be negative in value, the ratio may vary only between 0 and $+1$.

Between the extremes of 0 and 1, the ratio of the error variance to the total variance tells us the proportion that the variance *not* accounted for by the line of regression (the error variance of $Y$ from the line of regression) is of the total variance. The less the error variance—that is, the closer the association between water input and corn output—the more closely this ratio approaches zero. It is, therefore, desirable to invert the ratio by subtracting it from 1. After this operation the measure approaches 1 (instead of 0) as the solid lines become shorter in relation to the broken lines in our figure. It approaches 0 (instead of 1) as the solid and broken lines become more nearly equal in length.

All these paragraphs of explanation may be reduced to a formula for the coefficient of determination. Let:

$r^2$ = coefficient of determination

$Y_c$ = point on line of regression vertical to a given point of the scatter-diagram and

$\overline{Y}$ = mean value of the $Y$ variates

$$r^2 = 1 - \frac{\dfrac{\Sigma(Y - Y_c)^2}{N}}{\dfrac{\Sigma(Y - \overline{Y})^2}{N}},$$

which equals, in more familiar symbols, $1 - \dfrac{S_y{}^2}{\sigma_y{}^2}$.

When the numerator and denominator are each divided by $N$, the formula is simplified to:

$$r^2 = 1 - \frac{\Sigma(Y - Y_c)^2}{\Sigma(Y - \overline{Y})^2}$$

The foregoing explanation may seem to leave something hanging in the air. There a ratio was arrived at which indicates the proportion that the error variance is of the total variance. The subtraction of this ratio from 1 produces the coefficient of determination. By another approach the coefficient of determination may be obtained directly. In Figure 34 the relationships involved are translated into another graphic form that permits an alternative and more complete, if not simpler, explanation of the nature of the coefficient. By relating the following discussion to that figure the student may better understand what he actually does when he computes the coefficient of determination.

1. The dotted vertical lines in Figure 34, $Y_c - \overline{Y}$, represent the deviations of the computed values of $Y$ from the mean of the values of $Y$. They could represent, for example, the amounts by which the "computed" corn production on our irrigated plots diverged from the mean of the actual production. Or they would represent the variation of production if all production were fixed by the line of regression. This set of lines was not included in Figure 33.

2. The mean of the computed values of $Y$ is equal to the mean of the actual values of $Y$. Therefore, $\dfrac{\Sigma(Y_c - \overline{Y})^2}{N}$, the mean of the squares of the dotted lines, is equal to the variance (or the square of the standard deviation) of the computed values of $Y$. Here we smuggle in a feature missing from the preceding explanation.

3. The solid lines, $Y - Y_c$, are the deviations of the actual values of $Y$ from the line of regression. Their mean square, $\dfrac{\Sigma(Y - Y_c)^2}{N}$, equals the error variance. This could represent the variance of corn production around or from the line of regression or a measure of the differences between actual production and production if the line of regression or rate of water application had been entirely controlling.

4. The broken vertical lines, $Y - \overline{Y}$, represent the deviations of

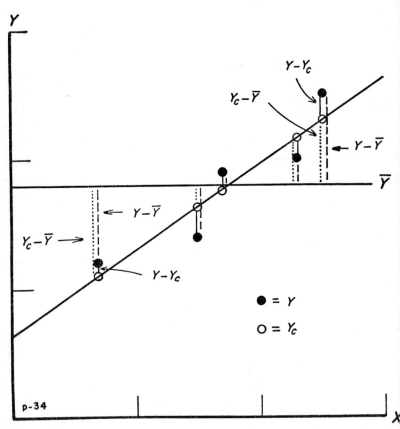

FIGURE 34

*An Alternative Graphic Explanation of the Coefficient of Determination*

actual values of $Y$ from their mean. The mean square of these deviations, $\dfrac{\Sigma(Y - \overline{Y})^2}{N}$, equals the total variance of $Y$. This could be a measure of the actual variability in corn output among our different plots. In practical research terms it is the variance to be explained or accounted for.

5. The coefficient of determination may be regarded as the ratio of the variance of the computed values of $Y$ to the total variance or

$$\dfrac{\dfrac{\Sigma(Y_c - \overline{Y})^2}{N}}{\dfrac{\Sigma(Y - \overline{Y})^2}{N}}$$

6. This ratio may be conceived as the coefficient of determination for the following reasons: It may be proved that the total variance of $Y$, $\dfrac{\Sigma(Y - \overline{Y})^2}{N}$, is equal to the error variance, $\dfrac{\Sigma(Y - Y_c)^2}{N}$, plus the variance of the computed values of $Y$, $\dfrac{\Sigma(Y_c - Y)^2}{N}$.

7. The formula given earlier for the coefficient of determination is:

$$1 - \dfrac{\text{Error variance}}{\text{Total variance}}.$$

By substitution it follows that an equivalent expression for the coefficient of determination is as follows:

$$\dfrac{\text{Total variance} - \text{Error variance}}{\text{Total variance}}.$$

8. Paragraph 6 states that the total variance is equal to the error variance plus the variance of the computed values of $Y$. Therefore, the total variance minus the error variance is equal to the variance of the computed values of $Y$. The variance of the computed values of $Y$ may be substituted in the formula immediately above as the numerator of the coefficient of determination, which becomes $\dfrac{\text{Variance of } Y_c}{\text{Total variance}}$, as given in paragraph 5. Now this relation-

ship for the coefficient of determination may be presented graphically, as in Figure 34, whereas the earlier procedure that arrived at the ratio by subtraction of another ratio from one did not permit a direct presentation of the ratios involved in the coefficient of determination.[2]

## An Illustrative Application of the
## Coefficient of Determination

A simple illustration of the coefficient of determination may be contrived from the data of the earlier scatter-diagram showing the relation between the Democratic percentage of the Maine gubernatorial vote (as the $X$ variate) and the Democratic percentage of the national vote (as the $Y$ variate). The coefficient of determination may be readily obtained by substituting the values derived earlier in the formula from page 113:

$$r^2 = 1 - \frac{S_y^2}{\sigma_y^2}$$

$$= 1 - \frac{7.985^2}{8.66^2}$$

$$= 0.1498$$

The earlier values also provide the figures for substitution in the formula for the coefficient of determination in paragraph 5 above, which is here simplified by dividing by $N$:

$$r^2 = \frac{\Sigma(Y_c - \overline{Y})^2}{\Sigma(Y - \overline{Y})^2}$$

$$= \frac{168.53}{1124.93}$$

$$= 0.1498$$

In this case the coefficient of determination, 0.1498, may be interpreted as meaning that only about 15 per cent of the variance of the national Democratic percentage around its mean was asso-

---

[2] The percentage of variance unexplained is known as the coefficient of non-determination. Its square root is called the coefficient of alienation, a usage parallel to the designation of the square root of the coefficient of determination as the coefficient of correlation.

ciated with or "accounted for" by the changes in the values of $X$, the Maine gubernatorial vote.[3] "Accounted for" has been placed in quotes to call attention to the fact that in this application the measurement of the relationships is not a matter of "accounting for" in the everyday sense of the phrase. The relationship may be conveniently measured or described by this procedure, but there is no question of a causal connection in the particular case.

This illustration also provides opportunity to mention a sharp difference between the properties of the coefficient of determination and the coefficient of correlation. The coefficient of correlation does not vary directly in value with the closeness of the association it measures; that is, a coefficient of 0.5 does not mean that the underlying ratios are half of those underlying a coefficient of 1.0. Mathematically illiterate persons, that is, most of us, think in terms of a scale of a 100 with 75 being a straightforward three times 25. The coefficient of correlation cannot be so interpreted. Hence, in terms of popular semantics one probably obtains a more meaningful notion of the relationships involved in the Maine data from the coefficient of determination, 0.1498, than from the coefficient of correlation, 0.387. It is useful while one is interpreting a coefficient of correlation to keep in mind the magnitude of its square. Thus with an $r$ of 0.4, it could be said that 16 per cent of the variance of $Y$ could be accounted for in terms of $X$; with an $r$ of 0.8, 64 per cent of the variance of $Y$ could be similarly explained.

*Another Illustrative Application: The Relation of Party Preference and Population Characteristics*

The Maine case presented essentially a question such as that of the relation between rainfall in Trenton and Philadelphia. The

[3] There is here, of course, an unnecessary crop of decimals, used in this instance to produce identical results by alternative methods. Curiosity about the arithmetic in the second formula may be satisfied by pointing out that $\Sigma(Y - \overline{Y})^2$ was obtained by squaring the standard deviation, 8.66, and multiplying by 15, the number of values involved in the illustration. The numerator of the ratio was obtained by substituting the known values, 7.985 and 8.66, in the equation in paragraph 6 in the text which indicates the total variance (the square of the standard deviation) to be equal to the variance of the computed values of $Y$ (the numerator above) plus the error variance (the square of the standard error of estimate), keeping in mind that the number of values was 15.

political tendencies affecting Maine and the entire nation were connected by a common origin rather than causally. A question of concomitant variations in more conventional form is raised by the data in the scatter-diagram in Figure 35, which shows the relationship between the percentage of the total presidential vote in each South Carolina county polled by the Dixiecratic candidate in 1948 and the percentage of the county population Negro. The supposition to be tested was that the higher the proportion of Negroes in the population of a territorial unit, the greater would

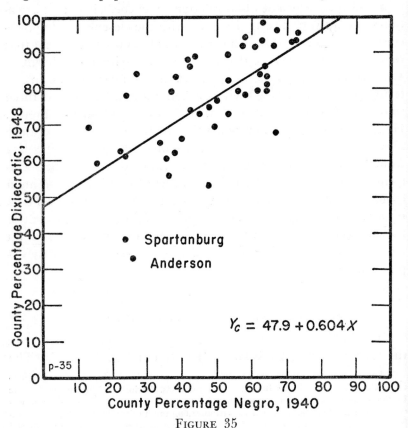

FIGURE 35

*Relationship between 1948 Dixiecratic Percentage of Presidential Vote and 1940 Negro Percentage of Population, South Carolina Counties*

be the propensity of the whites to vote Dixiecratic.[4] The scatter-diagram shows that a fairly high positive relationship existed between the two variables. In communities with high proportions of colored people, the white people tended to vote in high degree for the States Rights slate.[5] Yet a good deal of "unexplained variance" remains to be accounted for. The coefficient of determination for the data of the diagram is 0.45; the coefficient of correlation, 0.67.

The "unexplained variance," which in the South Carolina data is more than half of the total, is sometimes called the residual variance. The terminology is akin to that of one of Mill's canons of experimental method, which he called the "method of residues." He stated the proposition as follows: "Subduct from any phenomenon such part as is known by previous inductions to be the effect of certain antecedents, and the residue of the phenomenon is the effect of the remaining antecedents." Thus if it were supposed, "other things being equal," the Dixiecratic vote would have varied with the Negro population percentage, the "unexplained" or residual variance provides a measure of the lack of equality in "other things." In correlation analysis it is frequently possible to account for at least some of the residual variance by identification of particular points on the diagram and ascertaining their peculiarities. Thus in the South Carolina diagram some of the counties diverging most markedly from the line of regression contain within their boundaries considerable cities; an urban population, under the conditions prevailing at the time and place,

[4] In correlations between percentage variables descriptive of the population of geographical areas a source of error rests in the differences in the absolute sizes of the population of the units dealt with. Whenever practicable in the correlation of aggregates, the extremely large units should be broken into sub-units. The problem is most serious with respect to inferences drawn about the behavior of particular classes of individuals, e.g., because the percentage of farmers increased with the percentage of the Utopian vote, does it follow that the farmers voted Utopian? On the other hand, for other types of problems the size of the population of the unit may be immaterial. Thus, if the question is whether the "regular" organization can "deliver" the primary vote to its slate, each area may be regarded as a unit regardless of the absolute size of its vote.

[5] The uninitiated might suppose the diagram to mean that Negroes voted Dixiecratic. The interpretation of the chart rests on the assumption that a negligible number of Negroes voted, although the scatter was undoubtedly affected by the few Negro votes actually cast.

might plausibly be less disposed to go Dixiecratic than a rural population. All this amounts to a repetition of the suggestion at several earlier points, viz., that deviant cases in any sort of analysis may be of peculiar value in pointing to particular correlates of political behavior.

## 2. Computation of Coefficients of Determination and of Correlation

Computation of the coefficient of determination and the coefficient of correlation by the formulas used in their exposition would

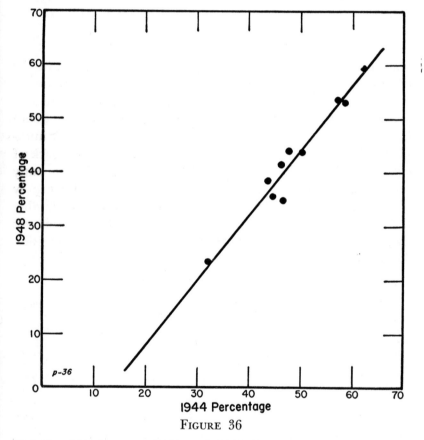

FIGURE 36

*Relationship between 1944 and 1948 Democratic Percentage of Major-Party Vote for President, New Hampshire Counties*

be unnecessarily laborious. Fortunately, mathematicians are adept at the contrivance of alternative routes to the same point. For-mulas exist whose execution produces the desired result more readily than it can be obtained from the formulas stating the nature of the coefficient most directly. The coefficient of correla-tion has been defined as the square root of the coefficient of deter-mination. Hence, only a single computational procedure is neces-sary to obtain either coefficient.

A formula, known as the product-moment method, for use in computation is as follows:

$$r = \frac{\Sigma XY - \dfrac{(\Sigma X)(\Sigma Y)}{N}}{\sqrt{\left(\Sigma X^2 - \dfrac{(\Sigma X)^2}{N}\right)\left(\Sigma Y^2 - \dfrac{(\Sigma Y)^2}{N}\right)}}$$

As a demonstration of the application of the formula, let us compute $r$ for the relationship between the percentage of the two-party vote in the counties of New Hampshire for Roosevelt in the 1944 election with the corresponding percentage for Truman in 1948. The data are plotted on the scatter-diagram in Figure 36. In the table below, the data are arranged in the form customarily followed in the computation of $r$. The $X$ variate represents the 1944 Democratic percentage; the $Y$ variate, the 1948 Democratic percentage.

| COUNTY | $X$ | $X^2$ | $Y$ | $Y^2$ | $XY$ |
|---|---|---|---|---|---|
| Belknap | 46.3% | 2143.69 | 34.8% | 1211.04 | 1611.24 |
| Carroll | 31.9 | 1017.61 | 23.4 | 547.56 | 746.46 |
| Cheshire | 46.0 | 2116.00 | 41.2 | 1697.44 | 1895.20 |
| Coos | 58.4 | 3410.56 | 53.1 | 2819.61 | 3101.04 |
| Grafton | 44.4 | 1971.36 | 35.8 | 1281.64 | 1589.52 |
| Hillsborough | 62.0 | 3844.00 | 59.7 | 3564.09 | 3701.40 |
| Merrimack | 47.8 | 2284.84 | 40.2 | 1616.04 | 1921.56 |
| Rockingham | 43.5 | 1892.25 | 38.7 | 1497.69 | 1683.45 |
| Strafford | 57.1 | 3260.41 | 53.7 | 2883.69 | 3066.27 |
| Sullivan | 50.2 | 2520.04 | 43.9 | 1927.21 | 2203.78 |
| TOTALS | 487.6 | 24,460.76 | 424.5 | 19,046.01 | 21,519.92 |

The value of the coefficient of correlation is derived by substitution of the values at the foot of the table in the computational formula as follows:

$$r = \frac{21{,}519.92 - \dfrac{(487.6)(424.5)}{10}}{\sqrt{\left(24{,}460.76 - \dfrac{(487.6)^2}{10}\right)\left(19{,}046.01 - \dfrac{(424.5)^2}{10}\right)}}$$

$$r = \frac{21{,}519.92 - 20{,}698.6}{\sqrt{(24{,}460.76 - 23{,}775.38)(19{,}046.01 - 18{,}020.03)}}$$

$$r = \frac{821.3}{\sqrt{703{,}186.2}} = \frac{821.3}{838.6} = +0.98$$

One needs only to square $r$ to obtain the coefficient of determination, which, in this case, is 0.96.

Other formulas for computation also exist. A variation on the formula applied above is as follows:

$$r = \frac{N\Sigma XY - (\Sigma X)(\Sigma Y)}{\sqrt{[N\Sigma X^2 - (\Sigma X)^2][N\Sigma Y^2 - (\Sigma Y)^2]}}$$

In the preceding chapter the formula for the coefficient of correlation was built up in a manner to indicate what went into the coefficient. An illustrative computation was made, using the New York registration and voting data, although it was indicated that the procedure was too laborious for ordinary use. If the student doubts that the computational formulas above will yield the same result as the formula of the preceding chapter, he may make a test by substituting the appropriate figures from page 80 in either computational formula. The result should be the same as that obtained by the earlier explanatory procedure.

There are various other short cuts in computation. In correlations involving large numbers of pairs of figures the data may be grouped for computation, a procedure for which is set out in most elementary statistics texts. Tables of squares and square roots, which may usually be found in standard statistics texts, also save no little labor.

Back to our example. Words of warning are always in order about the interpretation of the coefficient of correlation. The high coefficient from the New Hampshire data indicates that the points cluster closely around the line of regression. The sign of the coefficient indicates that the line of regression slopes upward, i.e., that the relation is positive. Beyond the measurement of the relation between $X$ and $Y$ the coefficient tells us nothing. Obviously the Democratic vote tended to be high in 1948 in the counties in which it had been high in 1944, and low where it had been low. Yet simply because the coefficient is high does not mean that there had been no change from 1944 to 1948; nor does it mean that the change, if any, was at a uniform rate from county to county. It may be supposed that the close relation represented in considerable measure the effect of the continuing or traditional Democratic vote. Yet close inspection of the slope of the line indicates that the "traditional" voters did not behave in the same manner in all counties although the $X$ and $Y$ relation is linear. In Carroll County, for example, a Democratic vote of 31.9 per cent in 1944 became 23.4 in 1948, a decline of about one fourth. In Hillsborough County, on the other hand, Democratic percentage dropped only from 62.0 to 59.7. The "traditional" voting group behaved differently when it was a local majority than when it was a local minority. As plausible an hypothesis as any might be that there must be a good many Democrats in a New England community for them to keep up each other's courage in the face of predicted defeat. Be that as it may, the statistical procedures only identify relationships: it is necessary to understand precisely the statistical nature of the relation so identified and then to apply ingenuity and perhaps other inquiry to the explanation of the established relation.

Interpretation of a correlation coefficient without plotting the data on a scatter-diagram is perilous. It may appear from a diagram, for example, that the relation between $X$ and $Y$ is not linear but curvilinear. Further, the slope of the line of regression may provide clues to the interpretation of the nature of the relation between $X$ and $Y$. Some of the observations in the preceding paragraph, for example, rest on the slope of the regression line rather than on the coefficient. Often the most revealing insights come from the points that deviate most markedly, and they can be identified only from the scatter-diagram.

## 3. Why Correlate?

The process of correlation constitutes one of the most valuable tools for the analysis of political data. Whenever the data relative to an hypothesis can be put into the form of a number of paired variables, the technique of correlation may be used in reasoning about the relationships involved. These limits of applicability exclude many types of problems of interest to the political scientist, such as phenomena of which few instances are available, phenomena comprising many more or less imponderable factors that can be disentangled by no mathematical procedure, phenomena about which the recorded or obtainable data are inadequate and so forth. Nevertheless a wide range of problems remain to which the procedure is adaptable, and often baffling and complex phenomena can be broken down into components susceptible of correlational analysis.

For the student of politics an awareness of the general mode of analysis and of reasoning involved may be considerably more important than mastery of computational procedures. In his speculations about all sorts of unquantifiable data the fundamental logical method has relevance. Even with quantified data often the simplest sort of analysis, such as a scatter-diagram, may be quite as adequate a tool for thinking about the data as extended calculation.[6]

Emphasis on the underlying mode of reasoning in correlation should make plain that significant results come, not simply from application of the technique, but from the hypotheses and relationships put through the procedure. Nor does the result of the computation have meaning of its own. The technique merely lays some basis for reflection and for verbal formulation of findings.

---

[6] The most elementary knowledge of the nature of correlation enables one at least to avoid some monumental boners. See Edward Pessen, "Did Labor Support Jackson?: The Boston Story," *Political Science Quarterly*, 64 (1949), pp. 262–274, and the comment by R. T. Bower, "Note on 'Did Labor Support Jackson?: The Boston Story,'" *idem*, 65 (1950), pp. 441–444.

After the completion of the calculation the real work must begin. What does the established relation mean in terms of the specific data? That alone is often a difficult question. But beyond that, what does the relation mean in broader terms or how does one formulate it in broader terms than the individual case analyzed?

In the correlation of the types of data available to political scientists all kinds of data can and must be utilized to describe and interpret the relation measured by a correlation. Sole reliance on the numerical data fed into the product-moment formula is perilous. In work relating to the electoral behavior of geographical units, for example, one needs to bring into the analysis every scrap of evidence to be had. In fact, experience develops a two-way working pattern. Correlation of statistical data points to inquiries to be made by interview and by examination of printed sources. In turn, such information gives substance to the correlation-centered analysis. The relations of a scatter-diagram often make relevant to the relation—or to specific deviations—random pieces of information apparently meaningless when they stand alone. And the correlation relation puts new meaning into data about particular cases. The case study can be made enormously more meaningful if it can be viewed through the framework of a correlation with other cases. Such an approach enables one both to "see" and to assess the significance of aspects of a case that escape one when it is studied in isolation. The meaning of these observations can probably become real only when one arrives at them independently through research experience, but they should be prayerfully considered by the beginning student—and the rest of us—when he bubbles with enthusiasm over the discovery of a correlation.

A question of practical tactics in correlational analysis is how to present the findings. To most audiences to which one directs his findings, the coefficient of determination or correlation is a symbol devoid of content. Often the entire conclusion can be translated into English and the statistical analysis discarded. Correlations of some types of political data can be presented in pairs of maps; transfer of the data to a map, of course, suggests additional interpretations that give new dimensions to the data. By the exercise of a modicum of ingenuity, the most hardened audience of skeptics about statistics may be seduced into following the findings of a correlation analysis. In the process it is often just as well to avoid employing the term correlation.

## A Note on Political Ecology

"Political ecology" represents, at least in some of its forms, an application of correlation analysis that warrants special mention. This type of study centers attention on the interrelationships of socio-political phenomena within geographical areas. The reporting of election returns by counties, precincts, and other territorial units permits analysis of the relation between voting behavior, as it varies from area to area, and the corresponding variations in characteristics of the electorate. At times the focus is on the relation between various social characteristics of areas and the division of opinion at a particular election. The Republican percentage of the vote, for example, might vary directly with income or rental levels. At other times the focus may be on the relation between social characteristics of the areas under analysis and features of voting behavior identified by time series of greater or lesser duration. Shifts in opinion from 1924 to 1928, for example, might be associated, from geographic unit to geographic unit, with differentials in religious composition of the population. The techniques employed in examining these relationships range from the impressionistic comparison of paired maps to multiple and partial correlation. Although most attention has been given to electoral behavior in this sort of work, the spatial aspects of other phenomena could very well be investigated by the same methods. Specialists in the field are known variously as political sociologists, electoral sociologists, electoral geographers; no political scientist or historian would be well advised to designate himself by any of these titles.

Political ecology rests on the analysis of aggregate statistics and suffers the disadvantages of all such analysis. Sample surveys permit the direct identification of relations between individual characteristics and individual political attitudes, whereas the correlation of aggregates compels indirect identification by inference.

Nevertheless, ecological analysis has its own special advantages. It throws data into a geographical framework that is often illuminating and it also invites attention to the historical dimension that frequently throws light on particular problems of inquiry. In fact, by ecological analysis dimensions of political behavior may be identified and examined that are almost impossible to reach by survey interviews. National or even state samples yield so few instances of many categories of voters that they may not be usefully analyzed. The behavior of such groups may often be studied in sufficient numbers by the analysis of precinct data to give one some confidence in the findings. Certainly a great deal of room remains for the enlargement of knowledge of American politics through careful and detailed "ecological" analysis.[7]

## References

### Method

F. E. Croxton and D. J. Cowden, *Applied General Statistics* (Prentice-Hall, 1939), chap. 22.

Mordecai Ezekiel, *Methods of Correlation Analysis* (Wiley, 2d ed., 1941).

F. C. Mills, *Statistical Methods* (Holt, rev. ed., 1938) chap. 10.

M. J. Moroney, *Facts from Figures* (Penguin Books, 1951), chap. 16.

A. E. Waugh, *Elements of Statistical Method* (McGraw-Hill, 3rd ed., 1952), chap. 15.

L. D. Upson, *Letters on Public Administration* (Detroit: National Training School for Public Service, 1947), chap. 4.

Pauline V. Young, *Scientific Social Surveys and Research* (Prentice-Hall, 2d ed., 1949), pp. 317–329.

### Applications

H. F. Alderfer and F. H. Luhrs, *Gubernatorial Elections in Pennsylvania, 1922–1942* (State College: Institute of Local Government,

---

[7] See Rudolf Heberle, "Principles of Political Ecology," in Karl Gustav Specht (ed.), *Soziologische Forschung in unserer Zeit* (Köln, 1951), pp. 187–196, and his *Social Movements* (Appleton-Century-Crofts, 1951), especially chaps. 10, 11, 12. For a reflective evaluation of French work in the field, see François Goguel and Georges Dupeux, *Sociologie electorale* (Cahiers de la Fondation Nationale des Sciences Politiques, No. 26, 1951). See also S. S. Nilson, *Histoire et sciences politiques* (Bergen, 1950).

Pennsylvania State College, 1946), chap. 3. Application of the rank-order technique of correlation, a method less satisfactory than the Pearsonian coefficient save for ranked data to which it alone is applicable.

Irving Bernstein, "John L. Lewis and the Voting Behavior of the C.I.O.," *Public Opinion Quarterly*, 5 (1941), pp. 233–249. Example of simple "correlation" without resort to complicated calculations.

R. H. Dangerfield and R. H. Flynn, "Voter Motivation in the 1936 Oklahoma Democratic Primary," *Southwestern Social Science Quarterly*, 17 (1936), pp. 97–105.

H. J. Doherty, Jr., "Liberal and Conservative Voting Patterns in Florida," *Journal of Politics*, 14 (1952), pp. 403–415.

H. F. Gosnell, *Grass Roots Politics* (Washington: American Council on Public Affairs, 1942).

———, *Machine Politics: Chicago Model* (University of Chicago Press, 1937).

A. H. Hansen and H. S. Perloff, *State and Local Finance in the National Economy* (Norton, 1944), chap. 2.

Rudolf Heberle, *From Democracy to Nazism* (Baton Rouge: Louisiana State University Press, 1946).

Rudolf Heberle and A. L. Bertrand, "Factors Motivating Voting Behavior in a One-Party State," *Social Forces*, 27 (1949), pp. 343–350.

Glenn E. Hoover, "The Political Diversity of Economic Groups," *Social Forces*, 11 (1933), pp. 415–417.

P. H. Howard, "An Analysis of Voting Behavior in Baton Rouge," *Proceedings of the Louisiana Academy of Sciences*, 15 (1952), pp. 84–100.

V. O. Key, Jr., *Southern Politics* (Alfred A. Knopf, 1949).

J. A. Kinneman and S. E. Shipley, "The Ecology of Pluralities in Presidential Elections," *American Sociological Review*, 10 (1946), pp. 382–389.

G. A. Lundberg, "The Demographic and Economic Basis of Political Radicalism and Conservatism," *American Journal of Sociology*, 32 (1927), pp. 719–732.

R. D. McKenzie, "Community Forces: A Study of the Non-Partisan Municipal Elections in Seattle," *Social Forces*, 2 (1923–24), pp. 266–273, 415–421, 560–568.

M. M. McKinney, "Constitutional Amendment in New York State," *Public Opinion Quarterly*, 3 (1939), pp. 635–645.

J. A. Neprash, *The Brookhart Campaigns in Iowa, 1920–1926* (New York: Columbia University Press, 1932).

W. F. Ogburn and Estelle Hill, "Income Classes and the Roosevelt Vote in 1932," *Political Science Quarterly,* 50 (1935), pp. 186–193.

André Siegfried, *Géographie électorale de l'Ardèche* (Cahiers de la Fondation Nationale des Sciences Politiques, No. 9, 1949).

C. H. Titus, *Voting Behavior in the United States* (Berkeley: University of California Press, 1935).

C. H. Wooddy, *The Case of Frank L. Smith* (University of Chicago Press, 1931), pp. 364–382.

C. H. Wooddy and S. A. Stouffer, "Local Option and Public Opinion," *American Journal of Sociology,* 36 (1930), pp. 175–205.

# 5

## MULTIPLE RELATIONSHIPS

Even simple linear correlation constitutes an extremely powerful tool of analysis. Yet the reasoning pattern inherent in the process of relating A to B in a linear fashion, whether one uses quantified data or relies on impression, contains hazards of which students should be warned. The pitfalls are obvious, once they have been described, yet students will find that their elders—including undoubtedly the author of this book—by no means always avoid them. The learned journals and the books abound in instances in which the unwary have allowed themselves to be trapped.

The logical structure of linear correlation—a pattern of thought used in non-statistical work as well—rests fundamentally on a comparison between two variables. Now, if factors other than the two variables remain "equal," all is well and good. Yet only infrequently does a single factor explain a phenomenon of interest to a student of politics. Failure to raise explicitly the question of the possibility that a third or even a fourth factor may enter into a given set of relationships often leads to erroneous or incomplete interpretations of simple correlations. Thus a simple correlation demonstrates no association or a low degree of relation to exist between A and B. Yet it may be that a third factor conceals a close correlation and that if "other things" are held constant, a uniform relation prevails between A and B.

Then there is the perverse tendency, most notable among columnists and editorial pundits but not unknown in academic circles, for the finding that B does not *always* follow A to form the basis for the conclusion that there is *no* relation between A and B. Often it may be demonstrated that A and B actually have the closest sort of relationship, if other "things" remain constant. Thus the theory is advanced that prosperity assures success to the party in power. Exceptions are cited; it is concluded that prosperity has *no* relation to electoral success. A little inspection of the exceptions to the generally prevailing relationship may lead to the discovery that other circumstances—a third variable—had special importance in them. One may be led then to a sharpened description of the relationship originally posited, a description that takes into account the kinds of circumstances under which economic prosperity favors the party in power, the circumstances under which other factors may offset that element of strength.

In other instances a high degree of association between two variables may be misinterpreted by a failure to see that the apparent causal or basic variable conceals or mirrors another or several other variables. Thus a high degree of association of voting participation with level of income prevails; similarly, the propensity to vote increases with level of education. Income level and educational level tend to be associated. In the explanation of differentials in voting interest is income or education to be regarded as the significant factor? Or does each variable have an independent bearing of its own on participation?

Obviously methods of analysis that would enable us to deal simultaneously with three or more variables or to separate out pairs of variables from the morass of reality and determine the nature of their relationships would be useful. This general problem has been implicitly recognized in the preceding chapters when attention was directed to the fruitfulness of a discerning examination of deviant instances in time series and in simple correlations. The assumption is that a third or other variable or factor has had a special effect in the sharply deviant cases. The identification of the deviates often suggests or leads to the discovery of additional factors operative in the relationships under inspection. The explanation of the sharp deviant is, of course, only the crudest sort of analysis, although it may at times yield results quite as adequate as do more refined methods. More systematic means exist for dealing with multiple relationships. They range from quite simple methods of cross tabulation to the techniques of multiple and partial correlation and factor analysis. These latter techniques require for their application a considerable knowledge of statistics. About all that can be done here is to indicate roughly their nature and the fact of their availability.[1]

## 1. Correlation by Cross Tabulation

Simple cross tabulation, although not strictly a method of correlation, has great practical analytical utility in the disentanglement of the relationships among several factors. Moreover, cross tabulation may be used to analyze some types of data to which the product-moment method of correlation is not applicable. In the preceding chapter the emphasis was on the relationships between variables, that is, characteristics differing in quantitative value. Often it is wished to determine whether an association

---

[1] Another broad approach has its uses as a means of simplifying the analysis of phenomena in which many variables interact. In the discussion above, the focus is on the problem of disentangling factors in the observation of real situations. Another approach is to construct, more or less a priori, "models" of behavior patterns. Thus a great deal of economic discussion consists of the analysis of "models" constructed on the basis of a series of assumptions about how "economic man" behaves. From these assumptions one may deduce the relationships among variables in models that include only the variables one wishes to reason about. Thus, if the drive to maximize profits is assumed and the existence of alternative points for capital investment is assumed, it follows that the variable of profitability will guide the flow of investment. By the exclusion from the "model" of many frictions and other factors operative in real-life situations, one arrives at an estimate of the relationships of the variables in question without having to solve the annoying problems involved in measuring the relative weights of a multiplicity of variables in a real situation. Now this sort of analysis is most useful, but it should not be confused with the observation and description of real behavior. Yet the model may serve most usefully in guiding inquiry. In a broad sense, when one makes observations or analyses of data to determine whether a "hunch" is true or to obtain the answer to a question, he is testing at least a vague sort of "model." A good deal of political speculation is in reality model-building although not often consciously or explicitly so. Certain assumptions are made about basic drives of political man and from that basis inferences are drawn about the types of behavior to be expected in particular types of situations. This type of analysis has its uses, but it is productive only of models and should not be taken for systematic observation and description.

exists between attributes or between attributes and variables. An attribute is essentially a qualitative characteristic present or not present. Thus the per capita expenditures of all cities of over 10,000 population is a variable, whereas the same cities do or do not have bicameral councils, an attribute. A voter does or does not regard himself as a Democrat, whereas the intensity of his loyalty to the party leadership could probably be converted into a variable by measurement on a psychological scale of some sort. A cross tabulation is only a tabular arrangement of data to indicate the association, if any, between characteristics. To show, for example, the relation between sex and average annual earnings of urban and rural-nonfarm workers in 1946, the data can be put into a table:

| SEX | AVERAGE EARNINGS |
|------|------|
| Male | $2,316 |
| Female | 1,130 |

The totals in the table may be broken down to indicate the association of other characteristics with earnings differentials. Thus, if education were a matter of concern, the following arrangement would be in order:

| SEX | | AVERAGE EARNINGS | |
|------|------|------|------|
| | Total | 7 Years Schooling | College: At Least 1 Year |
| Male | $2,316 | $1,746 | $3,178 |
| Female | 1,130 | 611 | 1,655 |

The precise form of the cross tabulation depends on the nature of the data under analysis, as will be indicated by later examples.

Cross tabulation is a simple procedure that requires little explanation, but it should not be dismissed as of little use because it is simple. Often a cross tabulation serves handily to show the association between two variables, between two attributes, or between a variable and an attribute. If two variables are tabulated, in effect, the data of a scatter-diagram are converted into a two-edged frequency table with stubs at the left and top margins of the table that group the $X$ and $Y$ values into appropriate classes. Such a table may serve adequately as analysis and also may be more readily communicated to some audiences than are other expressions of a correlation.[2] When the relationship to be tested is between a variable and an attribute or between attributes, cross tabulation may be the most suitable method of analysis.

## Separation of Variables by Cross Tabulation

At the outset of an exposition of some of the tricks of cross tabulation it may be well to belabor an elementary point. Students often have difficulty in grasping the notions involved in such propositions as, A tends to be associated with B, if other factors remain equal; or, if C is held constant, B increases with A. These are only re-statements of the basic problem of analysis that has been put forward in the immediately preceding pages.

Let us consider a concrete case. The National Opinion Research Center in 1944 interviewed a national sample of persons of voting age and ascertained, among other things, their economic status, the extent of their formal education, and whether they voted. When the respondents were classified according to their economic status, it was found that the following percentages of economic sub-groups said that they had actually voted:

| UPPER FOURTH | MIDDLE HALF | LOWER FOURTH |
|:---:|:---:|:---:|
| 85% | 69% | 54% |

From these figures it would be concluded that a tendency to vote was positively associated with economic status. The same respondents, however, showed the following percentages of voters when classified according to level of formal education:

| COLLEGE | HIGH SCHOOL | GRADE SCHOOL |
|:---:|:---:|:---:|
| 82% | 68% | 63% |

Here the level of participation increases at successive stages of the educational ladder. Since it is known that educational level and economic status are positively associated, the question could be

---

[2] For examples, see Key, *Southern Politics* (Knopf, 1949), pp. 455, 525.

raised whether the propensity to vote was associated with economic status or with educational level or both. The problem is to hold one factor "constant" or to "keep other things equal" while one examines a single factor to determine whether it has an independent association with the behavior in question. In this instance, a conventional procedure may be applied by classifying the persons who achieved a given educational level according to their economic status. When the grade school group was subdivided according to economic status, the following proportions of each sub-group indicated that they had voted:

| UPPER FOURTH | MIDDLE HALF | LOWER FOURTH |
|:---:|:---:|:---:|
| 83% | 67% | 54% |

Thus "education" is held "constant," at least if it is assumed that such differences in formal education as may have existed among the grade-schoolers may be disregarded. It would follow, at least for this group, that economic status had an independent association with the propensity to vote. The question then arises whether voting differentials were associated with gradations of education in the absence of economic differences. When the lower fourth in economic status was classified according to formal educational levels the following participation percentages resulted:

| COLLEGE | HIGH SCHOOL | GRADE SCHOOL |
|:---:|:---:|:---:|
| 70% | 54% | 54% |

When "other things," i.e., economic status in this instance, are held constant, education seems to make a difference but that difference sets in between the high school and college group.

The foregoing example should make plain the sort of operation involved in unraveling several factors by cross tabulation, but perhaps another illustration will clinch the matter. In his study of congressional voting behavior Julius Turner identified an association between several gross characteristics of the population of congressional districts and the voting records of their Representatives. In the process it was necessary to sort out the several constituency characteristics to establish the association, if any, of each with congressional voting behavior. One analysis, which appears in Table 2, indicated that Democratic representatives from metropolitan districts tended in 1944 to cluster in the higher levels of loyalty to party, as measured by the proportion of their votes with the majority of their party in the House. On the other hand, Representatives from rural constituencies clustered mainly in the lower ranks of party loyalty.

The student equipped with the most rudimentary knowledge of congressional politics will, of course, immediately raise the question whether the metropolitan-rural differentials in Table 2 are not in reality a mask for northern-southern contrasts. Turner had found that the voting records of Representatives seemed to be also associated with sectionalism and with native-foreign composition of the constituency. To test the question whether the metropolitan-rural factor had an independent association with voting records, he had to exclude or to "hold constant" the sectional and native-foreign factors. To do this he needed to compare the records of spokesmen of rural and metropolitan districts within

TABLE 2

*Metropolitan and Rural Pressures: Frequency Distribution of Metropolitan and Rural Democratic Representatives in Index of Loyalty, 1944*

| RANGE OF INDEX OF LOYALTY | METROPOLITAN | | RURAL | |
|---|---|---|---|---|
|  | Number | Per Cent | Number | Per Cent |
| Below 65.1 | 5 | 5.4 | 40 | 33.1 |
| 65.1–70.0 | 3 | 3.2 | 12 | 9.9 |
| 70.1–75.0 | 1 | 1.1 | 17 | 14.0 |
| 75.1–80.0 | 6 | 6.5 | 15 | 12.4 |
| 80.1–85.0 | 5 | 5.4 | 12 | 9.9 |
| 85.1–90.0 | 15 | 16.1 | 10 | 8.3 |
| 90.1–95.0 | 20 | 21.5 | 11 | 9.1 |
| 95.1–100.0 | 38 | 40.9 | 4 | 3.3 |
|  | 93 | 100.0 | 121 | 100.0 |

Source: Julius Turner, *Party and Constituency: Pressures on Congress* (Baltimore: Johns Hopkins Press, 1951), p. 80.

the South, since all of its districts were predominantly native-born. Table 3 contains the results, which indicate that the average index of party loyalty was considerably higher among Representatives of southern metropolitan districts than among Representatives of southern rural districts. Hence, under the prevailing circumstances, factors associated with metropolitanism pushed toward party loyalty, and factors associated with ruralism, or at least southern ruralism, pushed in the opposite direction. The metropolitan-rural factor had an existence quite independent of the north-south differential.

## TABLE 3

*Metropolitan-Rural Pressures: Average Indices of Party Loyalty of Southern Democratic Representatives with Varying Percentages of Metropolitan Constituents, 1944*

| PERCENTAGE METROPOLITAN | AVERAGE INDEX OF LOYALTY |
|---|---|
| 0–25.0 | 68.1 |
| 25.1–50.0 | 69.7 |
| 50.1–75.0 | 82.4 |
| 75.1–100.0 | 81.1 |

Source: Julius Turner, *Party and Constituency: Pressures on Congress*, p. 89.

## Illustrative Analysis of Correlates of Competition for Local Office

An example that deals with another kind of data may be carried through several stages of analysis to provide a peg on which to hang an explanation of several tricks of tabulation. This sequence of analyses grew out of some doubt that the democratic process necessarily carried with it a uniform and continuing degree of competition for power. The supposition thus became that there might be identifiable conditions under which competition for office was keen, other conditions under which the struggle for political status was less sharp or at least less obviously so. The problem thus became one of identifying the correlates of competi-

## TABLE 4

*Competition for County Office in Ohio: Offices Filled by Candidates Unopposed (at Either Primary or Election) and Offices Filled after Contest (at Primary, at Election, or Both) in Relation to Presidential Vote, 1944*

| COUNTY'S PERCENTAGE DEMOCRATIC PRESIDENTIAL ELECTION | NUMBER OFFICES | UNCONTESTED | | CONTESTED | |
|---|---|---|---|---|---|
| | | Number | Per Cent | Number | Per Cent |
| 20–24.9 | 9 | 3 | 33.3 | 6 | 66.6 |
| 25–29.9 | 54 | 24 | 44.4 | 30 | 55.6 |
| 30–34.9 | 117 | 47 | 40.1 | 70 | 59.9 |
| 35–39.9 | 135 | 56 | 41.5 | 79 | 58.5 |
| 40–44.9 | 207 | 62 | 30.0 | 145 | 70.0 |
| 45–49.9 | 144 | 30 | 20.8 | 114 | 79.2 |
| 50–54.9 | 54 | 6 | 11.1 | 48 | 88.9 |
| 55–59.9 | 36 | 3 | 8.3 | 33 | 91.7 |
| 60–64.9 | 27 | 1 | 3.7 | 26 | 96.3 |
| 65–69.9 | 9 | 0 | 0.0 | 9 | 100.0 |
| | 792 | 232 | 29.3 | 560[a] | 70.7 |

[a] The formal classification undoubtedly overstates the actual degree of competition for county office. Of these 560 contested posts, in 69 instances the losing candidate had become the nominee by being written in at his party primary, usually the Democratic.

tion for office or the variables or attributes associated with competition.

Inspection of the returns for elections of county officers in Ohio indicated that from county to county a wide variation existed in the extent to which local offices were contested in the direct primary, the election, or both. The proportion of offices contested at one or more of these stages of choice thus became a rough index of competition.[3] With varying degrees of competition for county office in 88 counties of widely varying characteristics the data were thus available for a search for correlates of competition for office.

[3] The offices analyzed included only those offices filled in presidential years and classed as "county offices" in *Ohio Election Statistics*. That classification does not include legislators or judges.

Other work had suggested that the conflict for the presidency had a powerful influence in the formation of state and local political groupings, that the national political battle tended to project itself into state and local affairs and to give shape to local parties. Hence the question arose whether competition for local office had any association with the closeness of the county vote in the presidential polling. The results of a cross tabulation to ascertain the relationship in 1944 appear in Table 4. The finding that stands out is that in sure Republican counties presidentially a large proportion of the county offices—about 4 out of 10—was filled without contest in either the primary or the general election. On the other hand, after the Democratic presidential vote exceeded 40 per cent of the total a much higher degree of competition for local office prevailed. The two phenomena were probably in considerable measure reflections of the same underlying factors, yet presidential politics may function as an independent factor in stimulating competition for local office, a proposition that might be tested if sufficient ingenuity were expended on the problem.

Often it is desirable to present a table in simpler form than in Table 4. The data of that table may be compressed, as in Table 5, to bring out starkly the broad contrasts demonstrated to exist in competition for county office under varying degrees of closeness of presidential voting. The telescoping of tabulations is a matter of art and of judgment rather than of rule. The particular groups

TABLE 5

*Competition for County Office in Ohio: Offices Filled by Candidates Unopposed (at Either Primary or Election) and Offices Filled after Contest (at Primary, at Election, or Both) in Relation to Presidential Vote, 1944*

| COUNTY'S PERCENTAGE DEMOCRATIC PRESIDENTIAL VOTE | OFFICES | | UNCONTESTED | | CONTESTED | |
|---|---|---|---|---|---|---|
| | Number | Per Cent | Number | Per Cent | Number | Per Cent |
| 0.39.9 | 315 | 100.0 | 130 | 41.3 | 185 | 58.7 |
| 40 and over | 477 | 100.0 | 102 | 21.4 | 375 | 78.6 |
| | 792 | 100.0 | 232 | 29.3 | 560 | 70.7 |

to be made can be determined only by inspection of the pattern that appear in each tabulation and by consideration of the featur on which attention is to be focused. Care must be taken, how ever, that the large categories into which the table is telescope do not conceal important exceptions and do not convey a fals impression of correlation. Thus, in making Table 5 from Tabl 4 one would observe that a sharp increase occurs in the proportion of offices filled after contest occurred at about the 40–60 division in the presidential vote. This gives some warrant for making tabular break at that point although the categories of Table 5 stil conceal some of the relationship involved. Incidentally, the rela tionship between closeness of presidential vote and degree of loca competition appears to be non-linear. In each category in Table below 40 per cent Democratic, the proportion of uncontested loca offices hovers around 40 per cent; only after the Democratic presi dential strength passes 40 per cent does the proportion of loca offices contested increase in a more or less linear fashion witl closeness of presidential vote.

In our quest for community or social characteristics associate with competition for office, let us assume that the closeness of th presidential vote either constitutes one variable or measures complex of factors associated with competition. Whatever the na ture of the relation may be, an association exists between close ness of presidential voting and competition for county office. Th technique of cross tabulation, as was demonstrated by the earlie examples, permits us to "hold constant" one of the two variable as we seek to identify another independent variable in the rel tionship. In the present instance the query arises whether amon counties with similar divisions in the presidential votes there ma exist variations in competition for county office. If such variation exist, with what characteristics might they be associated?

It might be supposed that social factors associated with urbar ization, such as the differentiation of class and group interest would provide a foundation for competition for local office. I Table 6 the classes of counties grouped according to closeness c presidential voting have been broken, in turn, into categories ac cording to urban population percentage. Close inspection of th

## TABLE 6

Competition for County Office in Ohio: Offices Filled in 1944 by Candidates Unopposed (at Either Primary or Election), According to County's Democratic Percentage of 1944 Presidential Vote and According to Urban Percentage of County's Population, 1940

(1) = Total offices filled in counties in cell.
(2) = Per cent of offices filled without contest.

| DEMOCRATIC PERCENTAGE PRESIDENTIAL ELECTION, 1944 | ALL COUNTIES | | URBAN POPULATION PERCENTAGE | | | | | | | | | |
| | | | 0–19.9 | | 20–39.9 | | 40–59.9 | | 60–79.9 | | 80–100 | |
| | (1) | (2) | (1) | (2) | (1) | (2) | (1) | (2) | (1) | (2) | (1) | (2) |
|---|---|---|---|---|---|---|---|---|---|---|---|---|
| 20–29.9 | 63 | 42.9 | 27 | 48.1 | 27 | 44.4 | 9 | 22.2 | | | | |
| 30–39.9 | 252 | 40.9 | 63 | 41.3 | 135 | 46.7 | 45 | 28.9 | 9 | 11.1 | | |
| 40–49.9 | 351 | 26.2 | 81 | 19.7 | 117 | 36.7 | 99 | 23.2 | 27[a] | 33.3 | 27 | 3.7 |
| 50–59.9 | 90 | 10.0 | 9 | 22.2 | 9 | 11.1 | 27 | 11.1 | 36 | 8.3 | 9 | 0.0 |
| 60–66.7[b] | 36 | 2.8 | | | 9 | 11.1 | 9 | 0.0 | | | 18 | 0.0 |
| Total | 792 | 29.3 | 180 | 31.7 | 297 | 40.4 | 189 | 21.7 | 72 | 18.0 | 54 | 1.9 |

[a] Crawford and Marion counties are the deviants.
[b] Category contains one county outside the range 60–64.9.

table will indicate the general principle of this sort of cross tabu
lation. A second tabulation of this sort makes possible some modi
fication of the initial inferences from the earlier table, which re
lated closeness of presidential vote and degree of local competition
The relationships that appear are a bit ragged, but they seem to
establish an independent significance for urbanism (a rather com
plex factor itself) in relation to competition for local office. If one
reads Table 6 from the top down, he finds that within each degree
of urbanization the proportion of uncontested offices usually de
clines sharply when the Democratic proportion of the presidentia
vote passes 40 per cent. Yet in the rural counties competition
increases most regularly with the closeness of the presidential vote
On the other hand, if one reads the table from left to right, th
relation between urbanization and competition is not so uniform
(with the presidential vote held constant), yet clearly in the more
urbanized counties, relatively high degrees of competition for local
office prevail in contrast with rural counties of similar complexion
in presidential voting.[4]

Table 6 presents a somewhat confusing picture and does no
highlight the findings. Although presenting the entire tabulation
as in Table 6, is better practice, stripping a table down to its bar
essentials is at times desirable. Table 6 could be reduced to th

## TABLE 7

*Competition for County Office in Ohio: Percentages of County Offices Fille
after Contest (at Primary, at Election, or Both) in Urban and Rural Counti
and in One-Party and Close Counties, 1944*

| DEMOCRATIC PRESIDENTIAL PERCENTAGE, 1944 | RURAL COUNTIES[a] | URBAN COUNTIES[b] |
|---|---|---|
| 0–39.9 | 54.7 | 74.6 |
| 40 and over | 72.0 | 84.5 |

[a] Those counties 0–39.9 per cent urban in 1940.
[b] Those counties 40 per cent or more urban in 1940.

[4] The observations in Chapter 1 about the construction of simple frequen
tables and their characteristics apply also to cross tabulations, which are only f
quency tables with additional dimensions.

form of Table 7. Here the telescoping of the table rested on the observation that competition for local office in the sure Republican presidential counties increased sharply after the 40 per cent level of urbanism was reached; similarly it increased sharply in the rural counties after a level of 40 per cent Democratic in the presidential voting was reached. The compressed table, of course, does not reveal the relationships in all their detail, yet it does indicate in blunt fashion that factors both of urbanism and of presidential competition are present in the original relationship shown in Table 4.

The relationships appearing in Table 7 compel a modification of the inferences that might be drawn from Table 4 about the association of competition for local office with the closeness of presidential voting. Since approximately the same degree of competition prevails in all the counties classified as urban, the data suggest that some factor or factors associated with urbanism conspire to produce a relatively higher degree of competition in these counties than in rural counties with a comparable closeness in the presidential polling.

Obviously the two factors examined do not explain all the differences in competition for county office among Ohio counties. In cross tabulation, if the number of cases is adequate, tests for additional variables can be carried on more or less indefinitely by further subdivision and cross tabulation of the cells of the table. For example, Table 6 contained some exceptions to the supposition that with the presidential division remaining constant the proportion of offices uncontested would decline with increasing urbanism. Two of the cells in the range of 30–39.9 per cent Democratic presidentially in 1944 appeared as follows:

|  | PER CENT URBAN | |
|---|---|---|
|  | 0–19.9 | 20.0–29.9 |
| Per cent uncontested | 41.3 | 46.7 |

Such departures, from a relation that seems otherwise to hold, invite tests for the existence of additional factors. Inspection of the lists of 1944 Republican counties indicated that a good many counties in old Democratic territory had moved over into the Republican column. The question thus suggested itself whether in those counties with a hidden Democratic past the ancient but diminished hosts of the Democracy might remain to challenge the Republicans in higher degree than in otherwise similar counties with an unblemished record of Republicanism. Those counties that gave a plurality to Herbert Hoover in 1932 were supposed to be in excellent standing in the Republical lodge. When the groups are subdivided along these lines the following results are obtained:

|  | 0–19.9% URBAN | | 20–39.9% URBAN | |
| --- | --- | --- | --- | --- |
|  | 1932 Dem. | 1932 Rep. | 1932 Dem. | 1932 Rep. |
| Per cent of offices uncontested | 31.1 | 66.7 | 38.1 | 54.2 |
| Total number of offices | 45 | 18 | 63 | 72 |

A tabulation such as this with its broad categories has a treacherous aspect in that it may conceal differences in one of the variables sufficient to account for the apparent spread between the cells. Thus the right-hand sub-tabulation above includes counties 30–39 per cent Democratic in 1944 and 20–39 per cent urban. The difference in the proportion of offices contested in 1944 in the 1932 Democratic counties and in the 1932 Republican counties could be a difference attributable to differences in urbanism, within the 20–39 per cent range, in the two groups of counties. A customary check is to determine whether the averages for the two groups for the characteristic in question differ markedly. In this instance the 1932 Democratic counties had a mean urban percentage of 30.8; the 1932 Republican counties, 30.1. Or it might be supposed that the apparent differences in the tabulation really reflected differences within the 1944 Democratic percentage range of 30–39. The mean percentages were 34.8 and 34.9.

Although the numbers involved are too small on which to rest a firm finding, party groups in the counties that were once Democratic presidentially may well remain to seek local office long after the county has moved over to the opposition in presidential politics. On the contrary, local opposition may tend to wither away, at least under certain conditions, in counties with extremely long records of attachment to one party in presidential affairs.

## Interpretation of Relationships Identified

A couple of morals need to be pointed. Tabulations and correlations do not necessarily mean much of anything in themselves. The Ohio tabulations, for example, began with a curiosity about the incidence and correlates of competition for power and led into an analysis of competition for local office. The relations found to exist take on meaning only through verbal translation into more or less general propositions. Competition for local office seems to be associated with the closeness of the presidential vote. The nature of that association needs to be thought about and, of course, also investigated further. At another stage urbanization also turned out to be an associated factor of considerable importance, which should lead to some speculation about the social and economic structure of urbanism as it relates to political conflict. Per contra, what is the nature of some of the rural counties that have relatively low degrees of competition for county office? Is there a discipline and a firmness to certain types of rural political structures that discourage those who would challenge the status of the governing elders of the community? Further, what of the rural communities in which a relatively high degree of local competition prevails? Does that competition flow from the remnants of groups that once controlled the community? Or are there other bases for competition for power? And, the data suggest speculation over a wide range of propositions that relate to the nature of the party group and to the incidence of competition for community control.

Yet another moral, no less important, is that the analysis of such quantitative data as in this example is only a beginning rather than the end of a task of research. Some students gain somehow the notion that all that one needs to do is to tabulate. The sample tabulations rather suggest inquiries into local history, into the patterns of western migration, into the sources of settlement of the counties, into the current composition of their population, and into a variety of other factors that might explain the relations found to exist. Such inquiries of course operate reciprocally in that they suggest additional correlations of the data to test the validity of additional hunches about what factors may be associated with particular types of behavior.

Skill in the mechanical chore of tabulation can perhaps best be acquired by trial and error. If large numbers of cases are dealt with, the data can be transferred to punch cards. If enough foresight is exercised to record on the card all the characteristics of each case that turn out to be relevant, producing with Hollerith equipment whatever tabulation seems to be promising is easy enough. More ingenuity in hand tallying is required to devise work sheets that simplify the formation of the cross groupings that turn out to be necessary. A practice that saves time in the long run is to be most meticulous in the recording of data. Usually tally sheets may be arranged so that accuracy in recordation may be checked by tests of internal consistency. Thus in the Ohio data the fact that each county filled nine offices provided a ready check on accuracy in recording the attributes of each office. If the uncontested plus the contested races did not equal nine times the number of counties in a cell, something was wrong. When a tabulation involves a variable, making the categories of the tally quite small is usually wise. They can later be combined and combining small groups is simpler than subdividing categories that turn out to be too large. Thus with a five-point class interval on the tally sheet, combination made possible the production of Tables 3, 4, 5, and 6. Where a main difficulty comes in clerical cross tabulation is in the subdivision of the first major set of categories tallied. The Ohio counties were listed by groups according to the closeness of the presidential contest with certain items about competition for local office indicated for each county. The urbanism cross tabulation then had to be made separately for each sub-group according to presidential vote. Sometimes instances can be tallied by several attributes, and the sub-groups according to these attributes may be subsequently used as they stand or combined into larger categories as necessity dictates. Thus the contested category in the Ohio material was a total built on tallies of winners by party and by the stage of the electoral process at which contest occurred. The same tally sheets could thus be used to produce cross tabulations (of the presidential voting categories) according to such attributes. The dedication of a little imagination to the layout of a worksheet before beginning the tallying of items usually is amply repaid.

## 2. Multiple and Partial Correlation

The preceding pages, in effect, raised the problem of the analysis of phenomena involving the relationships between several independent variables and a single dependent variable, although the discussion was not put explicitly in those terms. By tabulation the existence of these independent factors may be demonstrated, although that technique is quite crude. More refined methods for dealing with the same sorts of problems exist in multiple and partial correlation. An exposition of these techniques usually comes at about the end of a full-blown introductory course in statistics and, even then, their full development is left for more advanced study. All that can be done here is to indicate their availability and to explain most briefly their general nature. Unless a student of politics is prepared to delve rather deeply into statistics, he would be well advised not to attempt to apply these techniques.

*Multiple Correlation*

In its fundamental conception multiple correlation resembles simple correlation. In simple correlation the relations of only two variables were observed. $X$ symbolized the independent variable and $Y$, the dependent variable. By the regression equation $Y$ could be estimated from $X$. The meaning of that equation, $Y_c = a + bX$, was that in estimating $Y_c$, when $X$ increases by one unit, $Y_c$ increases by $b$ times $X$. The standard error of estimate gave a measure of the error in estimation of $Y$ from $X$. The coefficient of determination indicated the proportion of the variance of $Y$ accounted for by, or associated with, the line of regression.

All these features of simple correlation have their parallels in multiple correlation. Instead of employing the symbols $X$ and $Y$, the dependent variable is designated as $X_1$ and the two or more independent variables, as $X_2$, $X_3$, and so on. The problem is to ascertain the relations between the independent variables $X_2$ and $X_3$, on the one hand, and the dependent variable, $X_1$, on the other. Those relationships, as in simple correlation, may be described by a regression equation, which is conventionally written as follows:

$$X_{c1} = a_{1.23} + b_{12.3}X_2 + b_{13.2}X_3$$

The sequence may, of course, be expanded to include additional independent variables. This equation includes the elements of the equation for a straight line with some additions. The $a$, as in simple correlation, represents the hypothetical value of $X_1$ with the values of both independent variables at 0. The two $b$'s in the equation play a role similar to that of $b$ in the equation for a straight line. They are known as net regression coefficients or net coefficients of estimation. Each indicates the change in $X_{c1}$ associated with a unit change in an independent variable while eliminating variation accompanying other independent variables. Thus $b_{12.3}X_2$ would mean the variation in $X_1$ (indicated by the first subscript to $b$) associated with a variation of one unit in $X_2$ (identified by the second subscript) while $X_3$ (noted by the subscript to the right of the period) is held constant.

This matter of holding other things "constant" or "equal" is a descriptive quality of the procedure rather than a capacity to reach out and manipulate or control the phenomena under observation. In simple linear correlation a straight line was, in effect, set up as a model against which to measure the actual relations between two variables. In multiple linear correlation a different sort of model is set up; that model is, as in simple correlation, descriptively useful only to the extent that the relationships within the data approximate the sort of relations assumed in the model. A rough, rather than a technically precise, idea of the model may be had if one imagines a set of relations involving a great many instances of $X_1$, $X_2$, and $X_3$. Of this many instances, let us assume that a goodly number turn up with $X_3$ at the value of zero. The regression coefficient, $b_{12.3}X_2$, would indicate the slope of a line best describing the relation of an increase in $X_2$ to an increase in

$X_1$ in these instances. Let us suppose that another batch of instances turns up with $X_3$ at a value of 10. The same coefficient would also indicate, according to the assumptions of the model, the slope of a line describing the relation of $X_2$ and $X_1$ in those instances where $X_3$ was 10. The coefficient, $b_{13.2}X_3$, would describe the line of the model indicating the relation of $X_3$ and $X_1$ under similar sets of circumstances. In practice, of course, so neat a distribution of the independent variables does not often occur as has been assumed in these expository illustrations. The net effect of the arithmetic is that the independent variable held "equal" is held at its average value.

In its basic logic are hidden some factors that limit the kinds of phenomena that can be dealt with by multiple linear correlation. It is assumed, in effect, that the relations between $X_1$ and $X_2$ and those between $X_1$ and $X_3$ are independent, that is, that the relations between $X_1$ and $X_2$ are not affected by the value of $X_3$ and vice versa. Add a unit of $X_2$ when $X_3$ is at 10 and the effect on $X_1$ will be the same as if a unit of $X_2$ is added when $X_3$ is at zero. The model assumes that the independent variables are, in statistical usage, additive. If this condition is not approximated, the model implicit in multiple linear correlation is not appropriate for analysis of the data. A common example of non-additive variables is one in which $X_1$ equals the profits of an apple orchard, $X_2$ equals the profit per bushel, and $X_3$ equals the yield in bushels. If the value of $X_2$ is increased by 50 cents, the relation between $X_1$ and $X_3$, the total profit and the total yield, is materially affected. Add a thousand bushels to $X_3$ when $X_2$ is at 50 cents and the effect on $X_1$ is radically different than if a thousand bushels is added when $X_2$ is at zero.

The regression equation thus describes the relation between a dependent variable and two or more independent variables. Or it permits an estimate of the value of a dependent variable associated with values of two independent variables. If in the South Carolina example in the preceding chapter urban population were a relevant factor, estimating the Dixiecratic percentages of the counties could be carried out better from the Negro *and* urban percentages than from the Negro percentages alone. Once the values for the regression equation for a particular set of data are computed, an operation has been performed analogous to fitting a regression line in linear correlation. When only two independent variables are involved, their relationships with the dependent variable may be conceived of as a plane intersecting a cube. The slope of the plane in one way represents the directionality of the relation between $X_1$ (which may be regarded as represented by the vertical dimension of the cube) and $X_2$. The slope in the other direction represents the relation between $X_1$ and $X_3$. When more than two independent variables are involved, no simple geometric representation is feasible.[5]

As in linear correlation, the regression equation does not permit accurate calculation of all the values of $X_1$ from the independent variables. Or, all the points do not fall precisely on the regression plane. Some may be above it; and others, below it. A problem is thus created analogous to that of measuring the closeness of the points of a scatter-diagram to the regression line. Similar measures and relationships are employed in multiple correlation. The variance of $X_1$, or the square of its standard deviation, represents the total variance to be explained or accounted for. The variance of the computed values of $X_1$, that is, of $X_1$ estimated from $X_2$ and $X_3$, equals the explained variance. The unaccounted-for variance consists of the variance of the actual value of $X_1$ from their computed values. This is thus a measure of dispersion about the regression plane and is the square of the standard error of estimate, comparable to the measure called error variance in simple correlation. The explained plus the unexplained variance, as in simple correlation, equals the total variance of the dependent variable. The coefficient of multiple determination, $R^2$, is the proportion that the explained variance is of the total variance. It represents the combined effects of all the independent variables in "accounting" for the variance of the dependent variable. Its square root, $R$, is called the coefficient of multiple correlation. $R$ varies only between 0 and 1; as independent variables are introduced to explain more and more of the variance of $X_1$, the coefficient ap-

---

[5] For graphic illustration of the relation in several types of multiple correlation, see Waugh, cited in the list of references, p. 499.

proaches 1. Often $R$ is written as, for example, $R_{1.2345}$, with the subscripts to the right of the period identifying the independent variables.[6]

## Partial Correlation

The coefficient of multiple correlation and the coefficient of multiple determination indicate the combined effects of several independent variables. These summary coefficients give no clue to the relative weight of the independent variables. One method of appraising the significance of a single variable is by *partial correlation,* the general notion of which can be readily understood although its detailed computation and interpretation are something else again. Partial correlation is commonly said to provide a means for measuring the relation between a dependent variable and a single independent variable with other factors held constant, although this statement is tinged with poetic license. What the procedure actually accomplishes is a little less spectacular. Partial correlation builds on multiple correlation. Assume that the computation of a coefficient of multiple determination with two independent variables yields a result of $R^2_{1.23}$ equals 0.60. Let us add a third independent variable that produces an $R^2_{1.234}$ of 0.70. Of the total variance in $X_1$, 60 per cent was accounted for by independent variables $X_2$ and $X_3$, and 40 per cent remained unexplained. The accounted-for variance increased 10 points, from 60 to 70, by the addition of the third independent variable. This step accounted for 25 per cent of the variance unexplained (10 of 40) before $X_4$ was entered into the relationship. This ratio is the *coefficient of partial determination.* Its square root is the *coefficient of partial correlation,* which in this instance would be written, $r_{14.23}$, to indicate that it represents the partial correlation between $X_1$ and $X_4$ after the first two independent variables had been allowed for in the manner indicated. A similar coefficient could be computed for each of the other relationships, $r_{13.24}$ and $r_{12.34}$.

Only scattered applications of the techniques of multiple corre-

---

[6] All these remarks relate only to multiple linear correlation. The discussion becomes abstruse when the topics of multiple curvilinear correlation and joint correlation are introduced.

lation have been made to political data. The principal work among political scientists has been that by Harold Gosnell. Nevertheless, a wide range of opportunity exists for broadening understanding of the electoral process by correlation analysis. Sample survey procedures have advantages in this field since they permit a direct association of individual voter characteristics with individual voting behavior. Yet the reliance on survey findings by electoral analysts has concentrated attention on so narrow a variety of situations that it has given rise to generalizations that endure only until the survey of the next election. The vast quantities of electoral data on past elections would provide a base for more discerning general analysis of electoral behavior, although the care, ingenuity, and patience required in the application of correlation techniques need not be underestimated.

### References

*Method*

Kenneth J. Arrow, "Mathematical Models in the Social Sciences," in Daniel Lerner and Harold D. Lasswell (eds.), *The Policy Sciences* (Stanford University Press, 1951), pp. 129–154.

F. E. Croxton and D. J. Cowden, *Applied General Statistics* (Prentice-Hall, 1939), chap. 24.

Mordecai Ezekiel, *Methods of Correlation Analysis* (Wiley, 2d ed., 1941).

A. E. Waugh, *Elements of Statistical Method* (McGraw-Hill, 3rd ed., 1952), chap. 16.

Hans Zeisel, *Say It with Figures* (Harper, 3rd ed., 1950). Contains an extended treatment of the art of tabulation. See especially chaps. 4, 5, 6, 8, 9.

*Applications*

H. C. Beyle, *Identification and Analysis of Attribute-Cluster-Blocs* (University of Chicago Press, 1931). An exposition and application of a method for identifying groups of entities sharing common attributes rather than a conventional correlation analysis.

H. F. Gosnell, *Grass Roots Politics* (Washington: American Council on Public Affairs, 1942). In this and other works Dr. Gosnell has made extensive applications of multiple correlation analysis to electoral data. For a brief discussion of some of the advantages and limits of the approach, see this item at pp. 139–146.

Julius Turner, *Party and Constituency: Pressures on Congress* (Baltimore: Johns Hopkins Press, 1951). Contains many examples of ingenious cross tabulations.

# 6

VVVVVVV

# INFERENCES FROM

# QUANTITATIVE DATA

To round out this exposition of applications of the simpler techniques of statistics, some observations on the place of descriptive statistics in the field of statistics as a whole are in order; in this connection attention will be called to the character and uses of inferential statistical procedures that have not been dealt with. Mention of these topics will lead into a discussion of the nature of the process by which one moves from statistical description of the particular toward generalizations of wider applicability.

The journals of political science contain many treatments of the possibilities for the expansion of knowledge of political behavior by the use of statistical procedures. This discussion has been most animated and most prolix when it has been carried on, as it often has been, by persons who never sat at a calculator and tried to make sense from an incorrigible mass of figures. Unrestrained by the frustrations of experience, some speculators see in statistics a method for the solution of practically all questions. Others, untouched by the exhilaration of even minor discovery by quantitative analysis, scoff and assert that statistical procedures have no utility or at most enable one to establish by meticulous work only what he already knew.

Those who have made modest attempts to apply statistical methods arrive sooner or later at a view less cynical than that of the scoffers and less rosy than that of the starry eyed. In essence, statistical procedures only facilitate systematic observation. A great advantage of such a procedure is that it permits the perceptions of one investigator to be tested against those of another who follows the rules of analysis common to scientific workers. Data are arrayed comprehensibly, the process of reasoning is explicit, the limitations of conclusions are apparent, all of which characteristics are not invariably found in even the greatest intuitive works. Yet it must be recognized that many problems, because of the lack of adequate data, the fewness of observable instances, the difficulty and expense of observation, or the multiplicity of variables involved, cannot now be handled statistically. Vast areas of politics must be treated, if they are treated at all, by intuition, impression, sagacity, insight—all processes that are of the utmost importance but which yield results not readily verifiable.[1]

## 1. Descriptive Statistics and Statistical Inference

Although the simple types of quantitative analysis described in the preceding chapters are a part of the ABC's of statisticians, they constitute only one element of the system that gives the discipline of statistics its peculiar character. The techniques that have been set out constitute fundamentally only methods for describing masses of quantitative data (which of course record observations). Statistical description alone may be highly useful. Masses of figures may be reduced to a few mathematical symbols. Vague verbalisms may be replaced by more precise terms. Even perception may be sharpened, extended, and enlarged, for forms and relations may be identified that cannot be easily "seen" without statistical analysis. Intricate patterns of relations may not only be perceived; they may be described with some exactness. Yet when at long last the

---

[1] Nevertheless, the search for simple indices of the most complex and extended phenomena may not in the end be futile. See, for example a discussion of a possible relation between incongruities in the distribution of political and economic power and revolution and civil war by Fred Kort, "The Quantification of Aristotle's Theory of Revolution," *American Political Science Review*, 46 (1952), pp. 486–493.

final computation has been made in an application of descriptive statistics, all that one has is a description of the particular, which, of course, has its very real uses.

Statisticians take a step beyond the simple description of particular phenomena. Their chief interest as technicians centers, not on description of the particular, but on means by which inferences may be drawn concerning entire populations from the observation or inspection of relatively small samples. "Population," in the argot of the statisticians, has a meaning different from its everyday connotation. Populations are infinite or finite. All the carrot seed of a specified variety that have existed, exist, or will come into existence could be regarded as an infinite population. Other populations, such as all the bolts produced and to be produced by a given machine from given materials, may be treated as infinite. Finite populations could be exemplified by all the persons voting in Missouri in November, 1956, a carload of wheat, the employees of the Department of Agriculture on January 1, 1953, persons on the old-age assistance rolls in Montana on January 1, 1955, the labor force of the United States in April, 1954, or all 1957 model Fords.

All sorts of constituents, then, may make up populations. A type of population of special concern to statisticians might be called populations of measurements. Thus the percentage division of a sample in a poll on presidential preference constitutes a measurement, by estimate, of the corresponding division of the entire population, the prospective electorate. A succession of such estimates would constitute a population of measurements; an infinite succession of such estimates would be an infinite population.

The estimation of the characteristics of entire populations by the inspection or observation of relatively small samples is called *statistical inference* or *statistical induction*. From data concerning all instances within the population under examination, descriptive statistics yields measurements of the characteristics of the population—within the limits of the accuracy of the data and the mathematical computations. The aim of statistical inference is to estimate from the known characteristics of a sample the unknown characteristics of the entire population. These estimated characteristics are known as *parameters,* a term which, judiciously used, creates an appearance of erudition.

The great utility of any technique for estimating the characteristics of a vast population from the observation of a small number of instances is apparent. Much of the work of the Census Bureau rests on sampling, either in the collection of data or in the tabulation of samples from the complete census. Public opinion polls are a widely known application, yet many other uses of the technique occur daily in manufacturing, commercial, and scientific practice. A manufacturer of bolts, for example, undertakes to produce bolts within given limits of tolerance of tensile strength, or of length, or of diameter. An inspection or testing of all items is not feasible, but the quality control analyst by inspection of a small number now and then can estimate the characteristics of the entire flow of output. A medical scientist tests a vaccine by injecting a sample of 500 children with it and another 500 with an inert fluid. How can he assure himself that the differences in results between the two groups are significant; that is, that all children, the entire population, if so treated, will react in roughly the same manner as the experimental group? Here would arise an opportunity for statistical inference.

The mechanical task of drawing samples is to be sharply differentiated from the methods of statistical inference from samples. In many types of scientific work the characteristics of populations are such that the selection of a random sample presents little difficulty. If the mechanics of actual sampling may be ignored for the moment, the problem becomes one of suggesting simply, if possible, how to proceed from measurement of a sample to an estimation of the parameters of an entire population.

## 2. Sampling and Tests of Significance

The emphasis in most courses in statistics centers on statistical inference rather than on descriptive statistics. The object is to explain why and how the characteristics of a population may be estimated from a sample. The neophyte who picks up a statistics text to familiarize himself with the elements of the technique soon becomes befuddled by accounts of how many heads turn up in

5,000 flips of a coin, the theory of probability, the forms of distributions, confidence limits, fiduciary limits, tests of significance, the null hypothesis, and related matters. The impression may not be incorrect that in the social sciences extensive use has been made of such concepts and techniques without adequate understanding of their meaning. At this point it is proposed only to suggest in the most general terms the nature of tests of significance in order that some observations may be made about the relevance of procedures of inferential statistics in the analysis of political data.

Although the introductory treatments of statistics do not dwell on the matter, the process of statistical inference, in application if not in its theoretical foundations, rests on certain broad assumptions that, for lack of a better word, may be called more or less philosophical in character. Some of these assumptions concern the nature of phenomena whose characteristics it is sought to identify by statistical techniques. Thus in many types of work assumptions are made about the form of distribution of the instances of the population under examination. The normal distribution, for example, more or less fits many distributions occurring in nature. The heights of men, the mileage of automobile tires, the grades of freshmen, batting averages of baseball players, men's neck measurements for collars, weekly earnings of workers in a particular industry, age at death of postmen, and a thousand and one other such populations appear in the statistics texts as illustrations of the tendency toward a normal distribution. The frequency with which particular populations assume a form resembling a normal distribution is indeed striking. Obviously, to the extent that populations in nature tend to assume certain forms of distribution, be they normal or in some other recurring form, characteristics of entire populations may be inferred by the indentification of the characteristics of random samples.

An equally basic assumption in inferential statistics is that attributes of successive samples, in effect, populations of measurements, tend to assume a normal distribution. The means of a sequence of samples of a population, for example, tend to cluster in the form of a normal curve about the true mean of the entire population. On this and other characteristics of the distribution of populations of measurements is based an extensive system of estimating the probability that a given measurement of a random sample falls within specified limits of the corresponding measurement of the population under examination. Some writers use the term *universe* as an equivalent for *population.*

## Confidence Limits on Population Parameters

One type of statistical test has as its purpose the determination of the confidence with which we can say that a measure of a population, its mean for example, falls within specified limits from the corresponding measure of the sample. We have differentiated between descriptive and inferential statistics, but in a broad sense such procedures of inferential statistics are descriptive in their purpose. They seek to define the limits within which specified characteristics of a population may be described by measurement of a sample.

The nature of these procedures may be illustrated by a cryptic explanation of the procedure for establishing the reliability, i.e., fixing the confidence limits, of the mean of a random sample as an indicator of the mean of an entire population.[2] The requisite for a random sample, by definition, is that each item in the population has an equal chance or likelihood of being included within the sample. There should be no bias in selection. In the mechanics of drawing samples the actual approximation of equal likelihood or randomness of selection presents its difficulties, but assume for the moment that they have been surmounted. If a random sample of 100 cases were drawn from the files of 10,000 cases serviced by a welfare agency, the mean or average monthly payment to the recipients represented by the sample might be, say, $49.50. Another sample of 100 might have a mean of $50.51; another, a mean of $49.80. The problem of establishing confidence limits is to estimate the likelihood that the average of a particular sample falls within, for example, plus or minus $1.00 of the true mean or the average of all the cases in the files.

---

[2] The student who samples the writers on statistics will discover considerable diversity in terminology. Reliability and confidence limits have similar connotations, for example.

The procedure for setting confidence limits rests fundamentally on the normality of the distribution of measurements. If all the possible random samples of a given size were drawn from a population of a given variable, the means of the samples would approximate a normal distribution. This type of distribution occurs even though the distribution of the entire population may not be

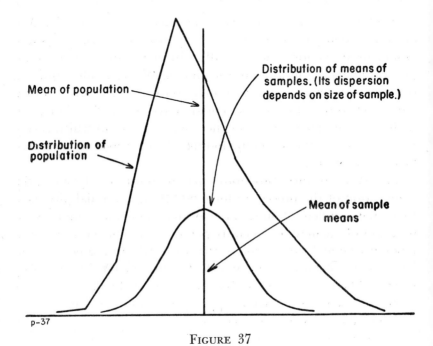

FIGURE 37

*Relation between Population Mean and Distribution of Sample Means*

normal. Certain characteristics of the distribution of the means of random samples, i.e., all possible samples, bear a constant relation to the distribution of the entire population. First, the mean of the means of the samples of a given size is also the mean of the entire population. This relationship is illustrated in Figure 37. Second, the standard deviation of the distribution of the sample means is equal to the standard deviation of the entire population divided by the square root of the number of cases in each sample, i.e., $\dfrac{\sigma}{\sqrt{N}}$.

From these constant relationships between the characteristics of the distribution of a population and the characteristics of the distribution of means of samples the reliability of the measurements by a particular sample can be estimated.[3] Obviously, from the constancy of these relationships, if certain characteristics of the entire population and certain characteristics of the distribution of samples are known, other characteristics of the population may be computed. To illustrate these relationships, let us suppose that it is desired to find the mean IQ of all high school truants. Let us make the unlikely assumption that the standard deviation of IQ for the entire population of high school truants is known to be 10 points. A random sample of 100 truants has a mean IQ of 95. With what probability may it be supposed that the mean of the population is within specified limits from the mean of the single sample? Since certain characteristics of both population and sample are known, from our constant relationships certain unknown characteristics may be obtained. From the standard deviation of the population the standard deviation of the distribution of the means of all possible samples of size 100 may be computed. This is $\dfrac{\sigma}{\sqrt{N}}$, where $\sigma$ equals 10 and $N$ equals 100. Thus the standard deviation of the means of samples equals 1. To this point it is known (a) that the mean of all sample means equals the mean of the entire population; (b) that the standard deviation of the sample means equals 1; that the mean of the particular sample is 95.

---

[3] The relationship between the standard deviation of the means of samples and the standard deviation of the entire population suggests a word of caution about Figure 37. In the chart the means of the samples appear to be widely dispersed about the mean of the population. Since the standard deviation of the sample means is equal to the standard deviation of the entire population divided by the square root of the number of items in each sample, the dispersion of the sample means would become less as the number of items in the samples increased. With large numbers of items in samples the dispersion of their means about the population becomes, relative to the population dispersion, quite narrow.

With these factors given, what is the relation of the mean of the particular sample to that of the entire population? It is necessary to revert to the nature of the normal distribution. In Figure 38 a normal curve appears with the area under the curve within ±1.96 standard deviations shaded. This shaded area constitutes 95 per cent of the area under the curve. It includes 95 per cent of the cases within the distribution. Let us suppose that the normal curve represents the distribution of the means of an infinite, or at least a very large, number of samples. The chances are

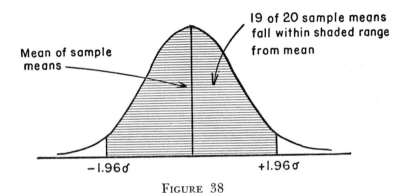

FIGURE 38

*Relation of Area under Normal Curve to Distribution of Sample Means*

95 out of 100 or 19 out of 20 that the mean of a sample drawn randomly from the distribution would fall within the shaded area. The probability that the mean of a particular random sample falls within specified limits around the mean equals the proportion of the total area under the curve between those limits. Let it be remembered that in random sampling each item has an *equal* probability of being drawn; 95 per cent of the items are in the shaded area; of an infinite number of samples, 95 per cent would have means within that area. Hence, it is said that the chances are 95 out of 100 that a particular sample mean would be drawn from that range.

Our particular sample mean came from a distribution of all

possible sample means that had a standard deviation of 1. The relation of that distribution of sample means to the true mean may be seen by supposing the small normal curve in Figure 37 to be shaded as in Figure 38. Thus, given the standard deviation of sample means at 1, the chances are 19 out of 20 that the mean of a particular sample falls within ±1.96 (that is, 1.96 times the standard deviation of 1, the shaded area in Figure 38) from the mean of the sample means, which equals the mean of the entire population. Since in our illustration we know the distribution of all possible sample means, we know the relation of that distribution and its standard deviation to the population mean. We do not know from what particular part of the distribution of sample means the mean of a particular sample comes. Yet given the relation of the sample means to the true mean, unless a 1 in 20 sampling error has occurred, the population mean, that is, the mean IQ of all truants, will lie between 93.04 and 96.96 (i.e., ±1.96 from the sample mean of 95). To use more technical language: At the .05 level of significance, the true mean lies between 93.04 and 96.96.

For expository purposes we have assumed an unlikely sort of case in order to indicate the constant relations between the mean of the population and the mean of sample means and between the standard deviation of the population and the standard deviation of sample means. The crucial step in the procedure was the calculation of the standard deviation of the sample means to obtain a measure of the dispersion of the means of samples around the true mean. In practice one never has the data to take that crucial step directly. Usually the data available relate only to a single sample. The number of items in the sample will be known, the standard deviation of the sample may be determined, and the mean of the sample may be calculated. Thus a rather different problem is presented than appeared in our expository case. There the standard deviation of the sample means (whose mean equals the population mean) could be calculated because the standard deviation of the population was known. The estimation of the chances that the mean of a particular sample fell within a particular range from the true mean was comparatively simple. To deal with the more usual problem procedures are available for estimating the standard deviation of the population from the standard deviation of the particular sample. From that estimate it is possible to perform the crucial step in the analysis and to proceed to an estimate of the confidence limits on the mean of a particular sample. Since the object here is only to suggest the broad nature of the process, the detailed procedures need not be set out. What results is not precisely an estimate of the likelihood that the mean of a particular sample falls within specified limits from the population mean. If the estimate from a sample turned out as in our preceding case with a 95 per cent confidence interval fixed by the limits 93.04 and 96.96, the true mean would or would not be between these limits. The degree of confidence, 95 per cent or 19 out of 20, describes the ratio of success or the expected relative frequency with which the sampling method would produce confidence limits that included the true mean. The finding would *not* be that the means of 19 of 20 samples would be expected to fall within the range 93.04 to 96.96. The limits of that confidence interval would be expected to differ somewhat from sample to sample.

An essentially similar method may be employed to define limits within which the proportion, i.e., the percentage division, of a sample approaches, within specified degrees of confidence, the true proportions of an entire population. As in sampling to estimate the mean of a population, the procedure rests on the relations between characteristics of the entire population and characteristics of the distribution of all possible sample proportions. The mean of the proportions of an infinite number of samples of a given size, for practical purposes a very large number of samples, is identical with the true population proportion. The essential problem reduces itself to one of estimating the distribution of the sample proportions, i.e., all possible sample proportions. The distribution of sample proportions does not follow a normal distribution but the binomial distribution. Happily, when the size of the sample is over 25 and the proportion of the sample possessing the given attribute falls between .20 and .80, the binomial distribution closely approximates the normal. Thus, if we assume that the distribution resembles a normal distribution, in the distribution of the sample proportions of all possible samples of a given size, 95 per cent of the sample proportions fall within plus or minus 1.96 standard deviations (of the distribution of sample proportions) from the true population proportion. Hence, if one needs to think in graphic terms, the problem may be visualized in about the same graphic forms that were employed in an attempt to gain an understanding of sampling to obtain an estimate of the mean.

All this information is not very helpful unless one is able to compute the standard deviation of the distribution of the proportions of all possible samples of size $N$. The formula for this standard deviation is as follows:

$$\sqrt{\frac{pq}{N}}$$

In this formula

  $p$ equals the proportion of the sample having a given attribute;
  $q$ equals the proportion of the sample not having the attribute;
  $N$ equals the number of cases in the sample.

An application will illustrate the formula. Let it be assumed, as is not the case, that the sample interviewed in the Gallup poll is a random sample. In California in 1948 Mr. Gallup's interviewers questioned 1818 persons, 52 per cent of whom expected to vote for Mr. Dewey. Within what limits could it have been said that the sample proportion approached the percentage division of the entire population? In a reasonably symmetrical binomial distribution when the number of items in the sample is sufficiently large, in 95 samplings out of 100 the true population proportion will fall within $\pm 2$ standard deviations (i.e., standard deviations of the distribution of all possible sample proportions) from the sample proportions. (Note that the range within which 95 out of 100 samplings fall, plus or minus two standard deviations, differs slightly from the range for a normal distribution, which was mentioned in the preceding paragraph.) If the number in the sample and the sample proportions are substituted in the above formula for the computation of the standard deviation of the distribution of sample proportions we have:

$$\sqrt{\frac{(.52)(.48)}{1818}}, \quad \text{or} \quad 1.17\%$$

Thus it might be said that at the 95 per cent confidence level the true Dewey percentage in California was $52.0 \pm 2.34$. Or that in only one out of 20 samplings would we expect the true percentage to lie outside the confidence limits fixed by the procedure, in this instance 49.66 and 54.34. It is also known that in a reasonably symmetrical binomial distribution, in 99 samplings out of 100 the sample proportion will fall within $\pm 3$ standard deviations (of the sample proportions) from the true population proportion. Thus at the 99 per cent confidence level the confidence limits are $52.0 \pm 3.51$, or 48.49 and 55.51.

The actual Dewey percentage in the California election was 47.4 per cent against Gallup's estimate of 52. Barring changes in voting intentions between the time of the poll and the election, as well as other such sources of error, and assuming that Mr. Gallup had a random sample, a percentage as far or further from the true percentage would be expected to be drawn less than once in 100 samplings.

The range around the true proportion within which the sample proportion may fall increases as the number of cases in the sample becomes smaller. Mr. Gallup's 1948 Texas sample consisted of 266 respondents, 24 per cent of whom indicated an intention to vote for Mr. Dewey. To estimate the 95 per cent confidence limits on this sample proportion, one computes the standard deviation by substitution in the above formula:

$$\sqrt{\frac{(.24)(.76)}{266}} \quad \text{or} \quad 2.62\%$$

The smaller sample results in a standard deviation considerably larger than that for the larger California sample. If 95 samplings out of 100 fall within $\pm 2$ standard deviations from the sample proportion, the 95 per cent confidence limits for the true Dewey percentage in Texas would be 24.0 ± 5.24. In fact, Mr. Gallup's sample percentage closely approached the actual percentage of 24.4. Incidentally, a little puzzling over the formula for the standard deviation of sample proportions will also indicate that the dispersion of sample proportions about the true proportion, with the number of cases in the sample remaining constant, narrows as the population proportion moves away from a 50–50 division. Similarly, with the true proportion constant, the dispersion of sample proportions narrows as the number of items in the sample is increased.

Graphic aids have been contrived that permit a close approximation of confidence limits of proportions without making the sort of calculations outlined above. With these aids it is possible to read off a chart the 95 per cent confidence limits for samples of given sizes and proportions.[4]

Other methods exist to determine the reliability of means and proportions, and special procedures are in order when quite small samples are used. Methods are also available to determine the reliability of other measures of samples, such as standard deviations and coefficients of correlation, as indicators of the parameters of entire populations. Enough has been said, however, to suggest the function of such techniques.

## Tests of Null Hypotheses

Tests of null hypotheses are closely related to procedures to establish confidence limits on the estimation of population parameters from samples. These tests in some instances simply refine the descriptive inferences drawn about populations from samples. In other applications, however, they are an important instrument in the estimation of the significance of differences in the behavior of experimental and control groups and, thus, an important instrument in the arrival at findings beyond description of the particular.

The essential idea of the test of a null hypothesis may be sug-

[4] For such a graphic aid, see John E. Freund, *Modern Elementary Statistics* (Prentice-Hall, 1952), p. 391.

gested without resort to a statistical formula. In August, 1952, the Iowa Poll conducted a survey of presidential preferences in Jasper County, Iowa. Of the men, 50 per cent (of 902) preferred Eisenhower whereas only 46 per cent of the women (433 cases) plumped for the General. From the preceding discussion of confidence limits, we know that repeated random samples of men would not produce a series of samples with the same percentage division but would result in a clustering of sample percentages around the percentage of the entire population. That true figure might well be more or less than 50 per cent. Similarly, repeated samples of the women voters would result in a clustering of percentages around the true percentage of the population, which might be more or less than the 46 per cent of the single sample.

In this instance a difference of 4 percentage points appears between men and women. The question is whether this represents a real difference in the populations or might be only a difference attributable to chance variation in the two samples. If the difference were attributable to sampling error, in another pair of samples the candidate preferences of men and women could be reversed. The null hypothesis is simply that the difference between the percentages of the two populations—men and women—is zero; in effect, the test of the hypothesis is a measure of the probability that two randomly drawn samples drawn from the same population could have the observed difference in proportions. If this probability is quite small, the null hypothesis may be rejected, although not necessarily disproved. A statistician has conventional probability levels at which the null hypothesis is rejected. The most common of these are the .05 level of significance and the .01 level of significance. If one abides by the first-mentioned level of significance, he rejects the null hypothesis if the difference between our sample values could be drawn by chance not more than 5 times in 100, if there were in fact no difference in the proportion or other parameter in question as between the two populations. If one abides by the .01 level of significance, the null hypothesis is rejected if the observed difference between our two sample values, or a greater difference, could be drawn by chance no more than 1 time in 100 if there were no difference in the population parameter in question as between the two populations.

In many types of scientific inquiry the kinds of questions put to the test of the null hypothesis are such that conclusions of great importance may be drawn. In the instance of the Jasper County presidential preference between men and women about the only possibility is to draw inferences about the men and women of that county as of the moment that the sample was drawn. One does not conclude that the difference is true of all men and women of the United States; nor does he infer from the sample to the "populations" of men and women extending indefinitely into the future. All one has is a test of the chances that the observed difference reflects a real difference in the male and female populations of the county at the moment rather than a difference that might be accounted for by the errors of sampling.

When some types of data and questions are tested against a null hypothesis, inferences may be legitimately drawn about the behavior of an almost infinite population, past, present, future. Thus if 500 children receive a specified treatment for diphtheria and 65 per cent of them recover while another 500 children are not so treated and 30 per cent recover, it is possible to test the hypothesis that the difference between the two proportions was attributable to sampling error rather than to type of treatment. The underlying reasoning is, of course, that the two groups constitute random samples of the same population except for differences in treatment. If the chances are low that the difference in proportions could be attributed to sampling errors, then one might draw inferences about very extended populations. For example, that the specified type of treatment would in the future, wherever and to whomsoever applied, result in a higher ratio of recoveries than would non-treatment. The conclusion becomes broader than an estimation of the reliability of the description of a particular population from a sample. Yet a little reflection will indicate that such a broad conclusion is founded only partially on statistical technique.

The basic question in the application of a null test is, About what population does one draw inferences? Failure to raise clearly this question and its implications lead to improbable conclusions from tests of null hypotheses. Thus, 20 third-grade children are instructed by one method; another 20, by another. Differences measurable by achievement tests are found to exist between the two groups. Tests of significance are applied and the results are extended to all third-grade children everywhere now and hereafter. Such reasoning is fraught with great hazard partially because one has no real reason to suppose that the two groups were at the outset random samples of the same population (i.e., that they were alike save for the differentials in instruction or, more precisely, that the differences between them other than the instruction were differences that could be accounted for by the spread between randomly drawn samples). Further, even if such groups were alike save for instructional differentials, he has no way of knowing that they were random samples of all third-grade children. Nor does he have any reason to suppose that future third-grade children will be the same as present third-grade children; nor that Italian third-grade children are the same as American or Canadian, and so forth. What results quite often is the projection without much warrant of the observations of small groups, of unknown characteristics and perhaps constituting samples of unknown populations, to extensive populations.

One also observes applications of significance tests that seem to indicate inadequate comprehension of the nature of the tests. On a given roll call in the House of Representatives, for example, 90 per cent of the Republicans vote yea and 15 per cent of the Democrats vote yea. The null hypothesis is tested and it is concluded that such a difference in proportions could occur by chance less than one time out of 20 and that the difference is "significant." One has, of course, a report on the entire population, i.e., the vote of the House on the particular roll call, and knows that the difference in the proportions, 90 and 15, is not a matter of chance. Then to what population does one extend the measurement of the sample? Does one regard the particular roll call as a sample of all roll calls that have been and will be taken, or of all roll calls of a particular session, or of all roll calls of a particular session on a particular type of question? Obviously, one does no such thing.

Most of the questions with which political scientists deal are not comparable to the example mentioned earlier in the chapter of the two sets of children treated differently for diphtheria. Rarely are the relevant variables in two situations so few that there is no need to worry much about the composition of the sample. Nor are politically relevant characteristics often defined sharply enough to permit much projection beyond the particular. The men and women of Jasper County in their differentials in presidential preference suggest the problem. The situation was defined in terms of relative preferences for Eisenhower and Stevenson. Conceivably, the situation might be defined in terms of attitudes of male and female under specified cultural conditions and policy circumstances when required to choose between candidates of specified characteristics. If such attributes could be both discerned and defined, it might make some sense to seek by appropriate tests measures of the probability that the observed differences existed in more or less infinite populations so defined. Yet it must be clearly recognized that null tests do not enable one to extend beyond the particular situation observations phrased in terms that can apply meaningfully only to the particular situation. Statistical technique alone provides no ready and easy way by which the general applicability of most conclusions from observations of political behavior can be determined. Yet an awareness of the nature of the technique of statistical inference, sensitizes one to the limits and possibilities in the formulation of generalization.

## 3. Simple Applications of Sampling

The argument has been that, given the present state of affairs, attempts by the political scientist to project, by means of statistical inference, his findings from the study of samples into universal laws do not make much sense. For some purposes a psychologist may regard a couple of hundred white rats as a random sample of an infinite population of white rats, that is, all the white rats of past, present, and future. The political scientist cannot very well extend his findings from a couple of hundred voters to all voters, past, present, and future. Yet such a reservation should not be allowed to obscure the fact that sampling and statistical inference can be extraordinarily useful in the descriptive study of particular populations. By this means analyses that would not otherwise be feasible became possible.

The most spectacular applications of sampling in the study of political behavior have been by opinion surveying organizations, such as the Survey Research Center, Elmo Roper, Inc., and the American Institute of Public Opinion. By interviewing a comparatively small sample of the entire electorate, such agencies have been able to enlarge greatly our knowledge of voting behavior. The sample survey is more useful as a means of identifying gross differences in the behavior of voters and the correlates of these differences than in predicting the outcome of elections. Even with a purely random sample, the odds against predicting the winner when the division is near 50–50 are quite high, an inherent feature of the polls not well explained to the public by the polling organizations. Nevertheless, survey findings identify differences among sub-groups of the sample that can be regarded with a high degree of confidence as indicators of differences within the entire electorate.

The individual political scientist ordinarily does not have the resources to conduct sample surveys of the electorate, although a few men have experimented more or less successfully with the conduct of local surveys with the use of student interviewers. In any case, to elaborate the problems of sample surveys would require several books, for a considerable body of experience has been built up by specialists in the opinion survey.[5] In problems other than those dealing with an entire electorate an elementary knowledge of sampling becomes quite useful in reducing research tasks to manageable proportions. Instead of studying a thousand cases, one may examine a hundred with quite as adequate results. The problem is simply to draw a random sample, which it might be well to define. A *random sample* is so drawn that each instance

[5] A good practical guide is Mildred Parten, *Surveys, Polls, and Samples: Practical Procedures* (Harper, 1950).

in the population has an *equal* probability of being included within the sample. The random sample is a particular type of a larger category of probability samples, that is, each instance in the population has a *known* probability of being included within the sample.

Political scientists frequently are concerned with problems that require the study of populations so numerous that all the instances may not be examined with the resources available. For example, there may be cited problems concerning all the towns of a state, all the members of a legislative body, all the employees of a Federal department, all the counties or townships of a state, all the actions taken by a court or other public body within a specified period of time, or other such populations. Simple techniques exist for drawing samples whose examination will yield results roughly indicative of the nature of the entire population.

The uses and limits of simple techniques of sampling may be illustrated by supposing that we wish to estimate certain unknown population proportions concerning the composition of the House of Representatives of the 82nd Congress. Let us ask: What is the proportion of Democrats in the House? What is the proportion of first-termers? What is the proportion of southerners (the Confederate states plus Maryland)? What is the proportion of New York staters?

We could, of course, tabulate all the members of the House according to these characteristics. The purpose of sampling is to avoid that labor by estimating the characteristics of the whole from the sample. To obtain a random sample of 50 cases from the entire membership of 434 (one seat being vacant) the mechanical task begins with a numbering in the order that they occur of the names on the list. Then the problem becomes one of selecting 50 numbers at random from the 434. Instead of rolling dice or drawing cards to select the 50 cases, a table of random numbers may be employed to select them. Such a table consists of figures jumbled together presumably in a chance or random fashion.[6] One reads down the table of random numbers, beginning at any given point,

---

[6] A table of randomly chosen numbers may be found in G. W. Snedecor, *Statistical Methods* (Ames: Iowa State College Press, 4th ed., 1946), pp. 10–13.

and checks off the list of Representatives those whose numbers correspond to the first 50 three-digit numbers in the table with values of 434 or less. In one drawing of a sample of 50, tabulations of the sample indicated that it included 21 Democrats, 8 first-termers, 9 southerners, and 5 New York staters. The problem, as first stated, was to estimate by sampling the proportions of the House consisting of these groups, which, of course, overlap. The sample contained the following proportions: Democrats, 42%; first-termers, 16%; southerners, 18%; New York Staters, 10%. How closely these sample proportions approached the proportions of the entire House will be indicated in a few paragraphs.

For a sample drawn at random, one may compute confidence limits and estimate the probability that the true population limits lie within specified limits. Such computations are not regarded as legitimate for a systematic sample, which is a little easier to draw. To draw a systematic sample one simply picks at random a starting point and draws every $N$-th item on the list. If one wishes to draw a sample of 50 from our population of 434 Representatives, he must do a little arithmetic trial and error to determine the starting point and the value of $N$. If one drew every ninth case and started with number 1, the last or fiftieth case would turn out to be number 442, more than the number on the list. If every eighth case were drawn, one could start with any case numbered from 1 to 42 and draw a sample of 50. In this instance a starting point was chosen between 1 and 42 by taking the first two-digit number between 1 and 42 from a column in a table of random numbers. That number was 31. The sample then consisted of Representatives numbered 31, 39, 47 and so on. In the sample so drawn the proportions were: Democrats, 52%; first-termers, 6%; southerners, 18%; New York staters, 6%.

Another type of sample is the so-called *replicate systematic sample*. Instead of taking one systematic sample of 50, one draws five systematic samples of 10 cases each. Each sample will have a randomly chosen starting point. The procedure is a little more complicated than the drawing of a single systematic sample. The value of $N$, the interval at which a case will be drawn, must be fixed so that at least 10 cases can be drawn in a sequence of 434.

The value of $N$ must also be fixed so that the range between possible starting points in the drawing of each sample of 10 will be maximized. What happens if $N$ equals 48? Since five samples are to be taken, the minimum range of starting points is 1 through 5 on the list, otherwise one sample would duplicate another. In the fifth sample the last case drawn would be numbered 5 plus 48 times 9, or 437. Since we have only 434 cases, 48 is thus too large an interval. If $N$ equals 47 cases, the last number drawn would equal the starting point plus 423. Thus by trial and error the largest workable value of $N$ is fixed. There is also a lower limit on the value of $N$. If $N$ equals 43, the last number drawn would equal the starting point plus 43 times 9, or the starting point plus 387. This value for $N$ would allow 47 (i.e., 434 minus 387) starting points. This number is not feasible because if in the random choice of starting points, 1 and 44, for example, were hit upon, two of the sub-samples would be almost complete duplicates. If $N$ equals 44 cases, the number of the last case drawn would equal the starting point plus 44 times 9, or plus 396 cases. This would permit a starting point from 1 through 38 (434 minus 396). Thus the interval can be fixed at from every 44th case to every 47th case.

To assure the broadest spread between sample cases, one should maximize the distance between starting points. If $N$ is fixed at 44, this condition is fulfilled. Five starting points are chosen at random between 1 and 38. In this instance those numbers turned out to be 16, 37, 15, 3, and 30. With these five starting points one takes every 44th Representative after each starting point. In the resulting total sample the following proportions occurred: Democrats, 56%; first-termers, 12%; southerners, 18%; New York staters, 14%. In general, the accuracy of the replicate sample should be about the same as a random sample but superior to that of a systematic sample. The establishment of confidence limits for a random sample is considerably simpler than for a replicate sample.

In the particular example, the proportions existing within the entire population are, of course, known. Comparison of the sample proportions with the known characteristics of the population indicates the kind of error that would probably exist if the samples were relied upon to estimate unknown characteristics of the population. Repeated sample drawings would, of course, produce somewhat different results. The detailed comparisons between known characteristics of the entire population and those of the samples are as follows:

|  | TRUE POPULATION PROPORTIONS | RANDOM SAMPLE | SYSTEMATIC SAMPLE | REPLICATE SYSTEMATIC SAMPLE |
|---|---|---|---|---|
| Democrats | 53.9 | 42.0 | 52.0 | 56.0 |
| Southerners | 25.6 | 18.0 | 18.0 | 18.0 |
| First-termers | 13.1 | 16.0 | 6.0 | 12.0 |
| New York Staters | 10.4 | 10.0 | 6.0 | 14.0 |

### 4. From Description to Generalization

The student of politics and government may be both legitimately and usefully concerned with simple description of the particular instance or situation. To know that the village constable of Pleasantville maintains a speedtrap may be highly relevant in delineating the impact of governmental authority in Pleasantville and have an important bearing on the ancient liberties of the citizen as well. Such questions of fact at points ranging from the United Nations to the smallest town in Vermont may have both relevance and importance for the student of politics, for in his day-to-day work he is called upon to prescribe what is to be done in such particular situations.

Yet the student of politics must attempt to go beyond the facts of the particular situation in quest of generalizations either in the form of rules or tendencies, if only better to deal with the particular problems with which he must cope. He would like to know, for example, under what circumstances constables in all the Pleasantvilles are most likely to operate speed-traps. Under what circumstances are constables in all the Pleasantvilles most likely not to operate speed-traps? And these questions might be expanded into the broader question of the circumstances under which those with authority are most likely to infringe the liberties of the citizen. The simple answer, based on a doctrine of individual perversity, may be to fire the constable of Pleasantville. To do that, however, might simply mean a reallocation to another worthy local resident of the revenues extracted from the unwary transient. Those with authority for action must continually make decisions that rest on the assumption that the relevant generalization has been established, that is, that they know what circumstances would be conducive to the maintenance or non-maintenance of speed-traps in all the Pleasantvilles.

## A Crude Analogy between Statistical Inference and Generalization

The question is, what place has statistics in the establishment of generalizations such as those about circumstances conducive to the maintenance of speed-traps? At the present stage of affairs, the answer probably has to be, "Not very much." Yet the broad theory of statistical inference throws light on the process of reasoning toward at least limited generalizations from the data we have to work with. The statistician attempts to proceed from his knowledge of a sample to an estimate, if not precise knowledge, of an entire population. At bottom, the problem of the constable of Pleasantville is to proceed from knowledge of the particular toward knowledge about the entire population of constables or even the entire population of law enforcement officials.

The problem of the constable of Pleasantville raises questions not often encountered in the work of the student in the statistically based sciences, although they are by no means absent. Those problems are essentially problems in the identification of characteristics of the population that are to be studied through the examination of a sample. Or the matter could be regarded as a problem in perception of the characteristics of the sample that might also be characteristics of a population. For example, one could, by the employment of discreet investigators, survey a sample of village constables and speed-traps. The survey might yield the finding that 28 per cent of all constables, within specified confidence limits, maintained speed-traps and 72 per cent did not. Other kinds of facts might be discovered about the sample, the proportion operating traps only during the tourist season, those with year-round schedules, the differential incidence in towns of different populations, and so forth.

Such a fact-finding survey would provide material for many Sunday features, but it probably would not give us our generalization. The statistical tests of significance would only tell us the limits within which the data could be relied on as descriptive of the practices of all the constables in all the existing Pleasantvilles. To move toward our generalization other kinds of data would have to be collected. Broadly, one would seek the correlates of a particular type of behavior, i.e., the maintenance of speed-traps by village constables. The trick consists in knowing or guessing what might conceivably be associated with the behavior pattern. One might want to know the types of incentives operative, e.g., is the constable paid by fee or by salary? What is his salary? Is he in necessitous circumstances? Is he, perhaps, a person with a sadistic streak? Is he popularly elected? Is he appointed, locally or statewide? Is the local government or the constable politically autonomous? Do statewide influences, either official or nonofficial, come to bear on his conduct? What is the nature of administrative supervision over him? What tribunal acts on his complaints? Is a speed-trap an intermittent affair in the locality or is it of long-standing? Are traffic signs legible? Are the rules themselves feasible of enforcement? And so forth.

What kind of generalizations would result from the examination of such questions one never knows. A plausible possibility would be: Locally elected officers compensated by fee tend more to discriminate against transients without local connections in the enforcement of traffic laws than do those compensated by a salary in excess of X dollars a month. Or fee-compensated constables might be found especially prone to discriminate in those communities in which the highway layout encouraged violation of regulations adjusted to maximize local safety and convenience in restraint of habitual and apparently reasonable habits of traffic flow. Or one might build the finding into some broader generalization about the fate of the stranger who encounters a local law enforcement official.

All this brings us around to the paradox that generalization may consist only in the most exact description of the particular. The most perceptive description of the particular may produce a formulation that itself describes a wider and wider range of situations or instances, which is generalization. An extension, to revert to our statistical analogy, may be made from the sample to the entire population. Or, at least, one may dimly perceive some of the characteristics of the population of which the cases under inspection are a sample.

## Identification of Significant Characteristics of the Particular

The process of identifying the significant characteristics of a particular situation, i.e., those characteristics that are controlling and would be controlling in other similar situations, is, of course, not aided by statistical techniques. Are there any ways by which one may think about his observations to increase the likelihood that he will identify these significant characteristics? A mental gymnastic that often aids in perception is to ask to what class of objects, attributes, or variables each element of the situation belongs. Thus, Joe Glutz, the unfortunate motorist, may be more than an outraged individual. Harvig Hefter, the constable of Pleasantville, may be more than a constable. To picture the situation as Harvig Hefter pinching Joe Glutz may not be very illuminating. If we assign the actors and elements of the situation to classes, we might have a needy and perhaps insecure person vested with public authority preying upon a person from without the jurisdiction to whom the fine costs less than the time to insist on constitutional niceties in its assessment. Classification constitutes a foundation for general rules of relationships and sequential patterns. And the type of generalization the student of politics seeks to establish describes sequences, relations, and associations among such categories.[7]

One must perceive before he can name or classify. A problem

[7] One needs be alert against the fallacy of supposing that once something is named it is classified for analytical purposes. The necessities of everyday discourse compel the application of a single name to varied phenomena. Hence, the advantages of specialized scientific vocabularies. "Vote" may, for example, have radically different meanings in different cultures and even different meanings within the same culture from time to time, place to place, situation to situation.

that besets the investigator is that of "seeing" all the relevant elements of a situation. Even the most competent investigator may produce a most learned and technically impeccable analysis of a situation and yet fail to "see" or to give adequate weight to a crucial element. Hence, prudence dictates that scientific inquiry be conducted with both humility and sharp eyes. The justly famed Erie County study[8] provides a classic illustration. One of its major findings was that extremely few people changed their minds about how they would vote as a result of the impact of the 1940 presidential campaign. Although the authors of the study did not extend their findings to the proposition that voters always did and always would in the main make up their minds almost immediately after the nominations and remain largely unmoved by the oratory of the campaign, others drew that inference. Hence, in 1948 pollsters and others predicted that, on the basis of the polls of September and mid-October, Mr. Dewey would win the presidency because it had been established by the Erie County study that voters' attitudes remain relatively fixed despite the events of a campaign.

After the election of 1948, a re-evaluation of the Erie County findings was in order. Obviously some crucial attribute or attributes of the situation had not been "seen" or identified or given adequate weight. One such attribute was probably the presence of Roosevelt as a candidate. As a candidate in 1932 and 1936 and as President for eight years, a relatively stable and structured set of attitudes or loyalties had been built up around him and the complex of views for which he stood. In 1948 another type of situation developed. Perhaps the analysis of the 1940 situation might be reformulated to produce a more complete description that, incidentally, would have wider application. That reformulation would probably indicate, among other things, that a campaign may change few votes when the majority nominee has already built up specified types of loyalties within the electorate.

The art of "seeing" the significant is never completely mastered either in the social or natural sciences. If it were, research persons

[8] Paul F. Lazarsfeld and others, *The People's Choice* (Duell, Sloan and Pearce, 1944).

in all fields would soon work themselves out of a job, for a great deal of inquiry results only in the amendment or supplementation of the findings of earlier investigators. The scientific world represents an odd sort of collective endeavor carried on by a highly individualistic organization. By the conduct of inquiry according to conventional rules and its careful reporting and systematic communication, the endeavors of one investigator may build on those of another.[9] One mark of a competent piece of inquiry is that it builds on relevant prior work and is in a form to permit subsequent addition or modification.

Are there any habits or patterns of observation that increase the probability that an observer will "see" the crucial elements in a phenomenon? An elementary requirement is that the observer be well acquainted with what is already known about his problem, that he be thoroughly familiar with the territory. The fresh look by the untutored mind at times gives new insights; perhaps more frequently it assures an insensitivity to obviously crucial factors. Beyond familiarity with the general terrain, a useful habit thought is to regard the individual, group, or situation under examination as existing in a field of influences or as at the center of a pattern of relationships. The inquirer can let his imagination play to identify elements in the field surrounding the point of inquiry and ask himself which of these elements might possibly have a bearing on the particular behavior under investigation.[10] In any particular situation the center of the "field" itself may also be located at alternative points better to bring into the range of vision possibly relevant elements.

Perhaps the technique of observation that contributes most to acuteness of perception is implicit in the logic of the experimental method. That method in its broad principles as they have been touched on in preceding chapters requires the compari-

[9] See W. S. Robinson, "The Logical Structure of Analytic Induction," *American Sociological Review*, 16 (1951), pp. 812–818.

[10] All these remarks do not mean that one concentrates solely on overt behavior. For some sorts of questions one must probe the motivations of participants in the situation under analysis but such psychological inquiry is apt to be misleading unless it is placed in its political "field" or setting. See E. Frenkel-Brunswik, "The Interaction of Psychological and Sociological Factors in Political Behavior," *American Political Science Review*, 46 (1952), pp. 19–43.

son of different types of situations. Now this comparison has as its formal purpose the testing of hypotheses about the significance of factors present in one situation and absent in another. Yet simultaneous observation of several situations also facilitates perception of factors in any one situation; in effect, the process suggests hypotheses to be tested. Thus crucial elements of the 1940 campaign in Erie County became apparent only after comparison with the campaign of 1948. Or one might contemplate the constable of Pleasantville for a period nauseatingly long and not see factors of the situation that become immediately apparent when one looks also at several other Pleasantvilles.

A closely related habit of thought helpful to perception is to break down questions for investigation. In political studies one is tempted or urged to investigate many questions that are really nonsense questions. For example, what is the effect of presidential campaigns? Who are the independent voters? What is the effect of prosperity on the chances for a party's continuance in power? What results from integration of authority in the hands of the governor? And so forth. All such questions make very little sense, and attempts to answer them are doomed to failure. It is helpful to assume for purposes of inquiry that the answer differs under different circumstances. The issue needs to be reformulated. If one asks what is the effect of presidential campaigns under a particular set of circumstances rather than what is the effect of campaigns, the acuteness of his perceptions may be sharpened no end. The problem is to break down the question for inquiry so that observation may be directed toward types of situations in which varying correlates of varying behaviors may be observed.

### Rising above the Plausible

Plausible generalization can be readily contrived without heed to the procedures of demonstration. Implicit in the preceding discussion has been the doctrine that the student of politics should attempt to rise above the merely plausible. The plausible generalization may be quite true. It may also be untrue.[11] The trouble

[11] See Paul F. Lazarsfeld, *"The American Soldier*—An Expository Review," *Public Opinion Quarterly,* 13 (1949), pp. 377–404.

is that there is no way of knowing which it is. Similarly, even the plausible description of the particular past event may be correct or incorrect.

A knowledge of the procedures of statistics sensitizes the inquirer into politics to the necessities of proof, although statistical techniques may not always be applied. Those methods of proof consist essentially in seeking to approximate the experimental method in the observation of political events. Only rarely may pairs of experimental situations be created, one with the factor whose influence it is desired to test and another without that factor. Yet the richness and variety of political events make readily possible the comparison and contrast of different types of situations. Experiments constantly occur before our eyes, although it may be difficult to identify the significant elements in "experimental" and "control" situations.[12]

In the analysis of these "experimental" situations in politics it is usually futile to apply the methods of statistical inference in projection of the findings very far beyond the specific situation. Yet in speculation about the general meaning of particular behaviors described in simple statistical terms, some of the theories of statistics are helpful instruments. Statistical emphasis on the behavior of aggregates is useful in politics as well as in actuarial science. One may not predict which of 10,000 individuals will die within ten years, but he can closely forecast the aggregate number who will do so. Similarly, statistical theory allows for relationships that are not necessarily invariant. Old-style scientific thought rested on the proposition that B invariably follows A. Obsessed with a belief that they must discover such invariant relations, some students of human relations prefer to rely on their intuition, rather than on systematic observation, when they contemplate the improbability of identifying invariant patterns of human relations. The student with a statistical cast of mind is satisfied if he can formulate statements of tendencies that seem to describe the behavior of aggregates but do not necessarily govern

[12] See S. A. Stouffer, "Some Observations on Study Design," *American Journal of Sociology,* January, 1950, p. 355. Also the discussion by S. L. Payne, "The Ideal Model for Controlled Experiments," *Public Opinion Quarterly,* 15 (1951), pp. 557–562.

in every individual instance. If B follows A in eight of ten opportunities, the statistician feels that he has made a discovery. Yet it must be conceded that at times he seems to claim that he has explained more than he actually has.

*Limits to Generalization*

In one sense the notions of inferential statistics point to a basic problem in reasoning about the general meaning of whatever data one analyzes, whether it be in quantitative or impressionistic form. That problem is the definition of the "population" of which the data we examine may be regarded as a sample. We see a recurrence of certain uniformities of behavior. Can we identify clearly enough the correlates of these uniformities to be able to describe the critical characteristics of the situation in which the same behavior will recur? That problem is, in its essence, the problem of generalization.

The quest for such uniformities, of course, causes raised eyebrows in some circles and, indeed, in the study of political behavior one must take into account basic limitations. Uniformities that one identifies, even by the most careful inquiry, probably are limited in their applicability to a single political culture. Further, the chances are that presently discoverable uniformities within a single culture can be relied upon to prevail only for relatively short periods. To hold to the contrary would be to contend that "human nature" never changes. There are, to be sure, those who contend that the autonomy of individual choices is such that searches for uniformities, that is to say, predictable behaviors, are futile to contemplate. Yet the hard fact is that uniformities of behavior, at least in the aggregate, do turn up with astonishing regularity. In given circumstances large proportions of individuals seem to exercise their "free will" in the same way. In fact, the process of governance operates fundamentally on the assumption of predictability of response to contemplated courses of public action. And perhaps a prime justification for the identification of uniformities of behavior is better to know how to change circumstances associated with those uniformities in order that behavior itself may be altered.

## References

Angus Campbell and George Katona, "The Sample Survey: A Technique for Social Science Research," in Leon Festinger and Daniel Katz, *Methods of Social Research* (Dryden Press, 1953).

H. C. Beyle, *Identification and Analysis of Attribute-Cluster-Blocs* (University of Chicago Press, 1931), chap. 4.

F. E. Croxton and D. J. Cowden, *Applied General Statistics* (Prentice-Hall, 1939), chaps. 12, 13.

David Easton, *The Political System, The State of Political Science* (Knopf, 1953).

Leon Festinger, "Assumptions Underlying the Use of Statistical Techniques," in Marie Jahoda *et al., Research Methods in Social Relations* (Dryden Press, 1951), pp. 712–726.

Oliver Garceau, "Research in the Political Process," *American Political Science Review,* 45 (1951), pp. 69–85.

Avery Leiserson, "Planning Problems in Political Behavior Research," to appear in *Political Science Quarterly.*

Philip J. McCarthy, "Sample Design" in Marie Jahoda and others, *Research Methods in Social Relations* (Dryden Press, 1951), vol. 2, chap. 20.

F. C. Mills, *Statistical Methods* (Holt, rev. ed., 1938), chap. 14.

M. J. Moroney, *Facts from Figures* (Harmondsworth: Penguin Books, 1951), chaps. 10, 13.

F. Mosteller and others, *The Pre-Election Polls of 1948* (New York: Social Science Research Council, 1949).

Hans Reichenbach, "Probability Methods in Social Science," in Daniel Lerner and Harold D. Lasswell (eds.), *The Policy Sciences* (Stanford University Press, 1951), pp. 121–128.

G. W. Snedecor, *Statistical Methods* (Ames: Iowa State College Press, 4th ed., 1946), chaps. 1, 8.

David B. Truman and others, "Selected Critical Bibliography on the Methods and Techniques of Political Behavior Research," *American Political Science Review,* 46 (1952), pp. 1033–1045.

# Appendixes

# APPENDIX A

# GUIDE TO SOURCES OF

# ELECTION RETURNS

### Basic Sources

Since the states are charged with election administration, the publications of the chief state election official, usually the Secretary of State, constitute the basic source of data on elections. Most states publish election returns in the state bluebook, manual, register, or comparable volume. These reports vary in their comprehensiveness and in the detail with which they report the data. An analysis of the coverage of the state publications appears in *State Documents,* No. 2, October, 1944, a publication of the Bureau of the Census. A serious gap in the reported data comes from the scarcity of published reports on the vote by subdivisions of the metropolitan centers. In a few instances the state reports break down the figures by ward or precinct and in a few others the city election authorities issue detailed reports, but such data must ordinarily be obtained by special inquiry.

### U. S. Government Publications

Several U. S. Government publications include compilations of elections data from state sources. The more important of these are the following:

*The Congressional Directory* is published in several editions for each Congress. It contains tabulations of the popular vote for members of the House and Senate, by district and state, for general elections.

*Vote Cast in Presidential and Congressional Elections 1928–1944* is a publication of the Bureau of the Census. The volume includes the presidential vote for 1940 and 1944 by counties with percentage computations. Similar tabulations are included for senatorial elections.

After each biennial election the Clerk of the House of Representatives issues a pamphlet entitled, for example, *Statistics of the Congressional Election of November 7, 1950; Statistics of the Presidential and Congressional Election of November 7, 1944.* The presidential year pamphlet contains the presidential vote only by states. The data on congressional elections in each biennial pamphlet is somewhat more complete than that of the *Congressional Directory*. The pamphlet may be obtained by request to the Clerk of the House.

The annual *Statistical Abstract of the United States* contains a limited amount of elections data: total presidential vote by parties since 1888, state by state presidential vote for two most recent elections, electoral vote for several elections, vote for senators, and vote for representatives by state. The 1908 number includes the presidential vote by states, 1888–1908.

### Non-Governmental Compilations

A few of the deficiencies in governmental elections statistics have been filled by private compilations. Among the more useful are the following:

H. L. Alderfer and R. M. Sigmond, *Presidential Elections by Pennsylvania Counties, 1920–1940* (State College: Pennsylvania State College Studies, No. 10, 1941). This publication includes tabulations of vote by county with calculations of percentage divisions among parties.

H. L. Alderfer and Fannette H. Luhrs, *Gubernatorial Elections in Pennsylvania, 1922–1946* (State College: Pennsylvania Municipal Publications Service, 1946). This includes, with some analysis, tables of vote for governor by county with percentages of party strength.

Louis H. Bean, *How to Predict Elections* (Knopf, 1948). The Appendix contains various tabulations of votes, the most useful of which consists of tabulations, by state, from 1896–1944, of the Democratic percentage of the two-party and total presidential vote.

David N. Camp (ed.), *American Year Book and National Register for 1869* (Hartford: O. D. Case & Co., 1869). It provides presidential election statistics by counties 1836–1868, both inclusive.

Francis Curtis, *The Republican Party, 1854–1904* (Putnam, 1904). This book contains the presidential vote by states for the period covered.

*The Gallup Political Almanac for 1948* (Princeton: American Institute of Public Opinion, 1948). This publication contains a miscellany of information, but the main body of the book consists of sections on each state showing the Democratic percentage by county in presidential elections of 1936, 1940, and 1944, the state total vote in congressional elections, with percentage division by parties for 1942, 1944, 1946, and the vote for governor for elections since 1928.

George Gallup, *The Political Almanac, 1952* (New York: Forbes, 1952). This book contains about the same data as the 1948 edition brought through the elections of 1948 and 1950.

————, *The Political Almanac with 1953 Supplement* (New York: Forbes, 1953). This book contains the material in the preceding title with addition of the 1952 results.

Alexander Heard and Donald S. Strong, *Southern Primaries and Elections, 1920–1949* (University, Ala.: University of Alabama Press, 1950). Herein appear county data on primaries and elections of governors and senators through the period indicated. Some series include percentage computations by counties.

E. E. Robinson has brought together the presidential vote by counties from 1896 through 1944 in two volumes: *The Presidential Vote, 1896–1932* (Stanford University Press, 1934) and *They Voted for Roosevelt, The Presidential Vote, 1932–1944* (Stanford University Press, 1947).

Jasper B. Shannon and Ruth McQuown, *Presidential Politics in Kentucky, 1824–1948* (Lexington: Bureau of Government Research, 1950). This publication contains the county by county vote for each presidential election, the percentage division by parties by county, and the participation rates by counties, together with a brief essay on each election.

The *World Almanac* contains county figures on presidential elections. It is the compilation with this coverage first available after each presidential election.

# APPENDIX B

# EXERCISES

## Chapter 1

1. Obtain from the *Congressional Quarterly Almanac* the party-unity percentages of the members of the United States Senate for a recent session of Congress. Prepare a frequency table for each party group; use 10 point classes. Present the distributions as frequency polygons. Determine the mean and median party-unity percentages for each party group. In the light of the measures of central tendency and of the frequency distributions, compare the cohesiveness of the party groups. Note whether the identification of the Senators whose scores fall at the extremes of each distribution gives a clue to the nature of internal cleavages within the party.

2. A comparative analysis of behavior of party groups in House and Senate may be made if frequency distributions of party-unity percentages for Democratic and Republican groups in the House are also prepared. Ascertain the mean and median of each House party group. Do these measures serve adequately to compare Senate and House groups? Does a comparison of the frequency polygons of House and Senate groups make possible more meaningful comparisons than the use of measures of central tendency alone? Compute the coefficient of deviation for each Senate and House group. What additional contrasts does this figure bring to light? Write a few paragraphs indicating your explanations for the contrasts and similarities that you find to exist between party groups

| DISTRICT | 1948 GENERAL ELECTION Per Cent Democratic[a] | Per Cent Republican | 1908 PER CENT DEMOCRATIC | DISTRICT | 1948 GENERAL ELECTION Per Cent Democratic[a] | Per Cent Republican | 1908 PER CENT DEMOCRATIC |
|---|---|---|---|---|---|---|---|
| Adair | 48.1 | 51.9 † | 43.8 | Dent | 58.6 | 41.4 | 50.8 |
| Andrew | 0.0 | 100.0 † | 44.8 | Douglas | 27.5 | 72.5 | 35.2 |
| Atchison | 0.0 | 100.0 † | 51.2 | Dunklin | 100.0 * † | 0.0 | 61.8 |
| Audrain | 74.4 * | 25.6 | 66.4 | Franklin | 50.3 | 49.7 † | 38.1 |
| Barry | 0.0 | 100.0 * † | 50.9 | Gasconade | 0.0 | 100.0 * † | 0.0 |
| Barton | 53.5 * | 46.5 | 53.3 | Gentry | 59.3 * † | 40.7 | 54.3 |
| Bates | 50.9 | 49.1 † | 55.0 | Greene I | 45.7 | 54.3 * † | 51.0 |
| Benton | 35.1 | 64.9 * † | 42.5 | Greene II | 56.8 * | 43.2 * † | 44.6 |
| Bollinger | 48.7 | 51.3 * † | 48.5 | Greene III | 55.6 | 44.4 † | . . . |
| Boone | 75.8 † | 24.2 | 70.7 | Grundy | 0.0 | 100.0 † | 35.8 |
| Buchanan I | 55.6 | 44.4 † | 47.6 | Harrison | 0.0 | 100.0 * † | 40.4 |
| Buchanan II | 62.0 * | 38.0 * | 56.9 | Henry | 61.2 | 38.8 | 54.7 |
| Buchanan III | 70.0 * † | 30.0 | 100.0 | Hickory | 0.0 | 100.0 † | 35.0 |
| Buchanan IV | . . . | . . . | 53.9 | Holt | 0.0 | 100.0 * † | 42.4 |
| Butler | 57.0 | 43.0 * † | 46.0 | Howard | 100.0 † | 0.0 | 70.8 |
| Caldwell | 0.0 | 100.0 † | 45.7 | Howell | 41.0 | 59.0 * † | 46.0 |
| Callaway | 73.5 * † | 26.5 | 67.3 | Iron | 66.0 * † | 34.0 | 52.2 |
| Camden | 0.0 | 100.0 * † | 40.1 | Jackson I | 81.1 * | 18.9 | 61.2 |
| Cape Girardeau | 53.2 | 46.8 | 46.4 | Jackson II | 79.3 * | 20.7 | 50.5 |
| Carroll | 48.5 | 51.5 † | 49.1 | Jackson III | 69.9 * † | 30.1 | 56.3 |
| Carter | 59.5 † | 40.5 * | 53.9 | Jackson IV | 69.5 † | 30.5 * | 65.8 |
| Cass | 58.8 | 41.2 | 58.0 | Jackson V | 61.3 * | 38.7 * † | 53.5 |
| Cedar | 39.8 | 60.2 † | 43.7 | Jackson VI | 54.1 * | 45.9 * | 54.4 |
| Chariton | 64.0 † | 36.0 | 59.5 | Jackson VII | 46.9 * | 53.1 † | . . . |
| Christian | 0.0 | 100.0 * † | 33.2 | Jackson VIII | 57.6 * | 42.4 * † | . . . |
| Clark | 51.3 | 48.7 * | 50.4 | Jackson IX | 60.8 * | 39.2 * † | . . . |
| Clay | 67.2 * † | 32.8 | 75.7 | Jackson X | 36.8 | 63.2 † | . . . |
| Clinton | 65.3 * | 34.7 | 56.5 | Jackson XI | 63.9 * † | 36.1 | . . . |
| Cole | 48.2 | 51.8 † | 49.9 | Jasper I | 0.0 | 100.0 * † | 45.8 |
| Cooper | 0.0 | 100.0 † | 49.9 | Jasper II | 54.7 | 45.3 † | 51.5 |
| Crawford | 00.2 | 99.8 * † | 45.7 | Jasper III | 49.3 | 50.7 * † | 46.3 |
| Dade | 36.1 | 63.9 * † | 42.7 | Jefferson | 61.6 * | 38.4 | 47.8 |
| Dallas | 36.2 | 63.8 * † | 40.5 | Johnson | 50.8 | 49.2 † | 52.8 |
| Daviess | 48.2 | 51.8 * † | 48.9 | Knox | 57.7 | 42.3 † | 49.5 |
| De Kalb | 46.2 | 53.8 † | 49.5 | Laclede | 40.0 | 60.0 * † | 44.5 |

[a] Percentages are of the two-party vote.

| DISTRICT | 1948 GENERAL ELECTION Per Cent Democratic[a] | Per Cent Republican | 1908 PER CENT DEMOCRATIC | DISTRICT | 1948 GENERAL ELECTION Per Cent Democratic[a] | Per Cent Republican | 1908 PER CENT DEMOCRATIC |
|---|---|---|---|---|---|---|---|
| Lafayette | 50.1 | 49.9 † | 49.8 | Ray | 100.0 † | 0.0 | 61.0 |
| Lawrence | 45.5 | 54.5 | 47.6 | Reynolds | 100.0 * † | 0.0 | 65.9 |
| Lewis | 70.9 † | 29.1 | 62.1 | Ripley | 55.8 | 44.2 † | 55.4 |
| Lincoln | 100.0 † | 0.0 | 61.7 | St. Charles | 48.9 | 51.1 * | 35.7 |
| Linn | 58.2 * | 41.8 * | 50.4 | St. Clair | 52.4 | 47.6 † | 51.9 |
| | | | | | | | |
| Livingston | 49.2 | 50.8 | 49.1 | St. Francois | 72.5 | 27.5 * † | 48.5 |
| McDonald | 47.3 | 52.7 * † | 48.4 | Ste. Genevieve | 0.0 | 100.0 † | 53.0 |
| Macon | 52.7 | 47.3 † | 52.4 | St. Louis County I | 54.6 | 45.4 † | 37.3 |
| Madison | 56.1 | 43.9 * † | 49.3 | St. Louis County II | 50.5 | 49.5 * † | 23.9 |
| Maries | 100.0 * | 0.0 | 64.0 | St. Louis County III | 46.4 | 53.6 † | . . . |
| | | | | | | | |
| Marion | 100.0 † | 0.0 | 61.3 | St. Louis County IV | 37.2 | 62.8 † | . . . |
| Mercer | 37.6 | 62.4 * | 0.0 | St. Louis County V | 43.4 | 56.6 † | . . . |
| Miller | 0.0 | 100.0 † | 38.4 | St. Louis County VI | 40.2 | 59.8 † | . . . |
| Mississippi | 100.0 * † | 0.0 | 54.6 | St. Louis County VII | 35.4 | 64.6 † | . . . |
| Moniteau | 53.9 | 46.1 * † | 52.1 | Saline | 63.6 † | 36.4 | 59.2 |
| | | | | | | | |
| Monroe | 86.5 * † | 13.5 | 81.4 | Schuyler | 54.6 † | 45.4 | 53.6 |
| Montgomery | 0.0 | 100.0 † | 51.3 | Scotland | 50.6 | 49.4 † | 51.7 |
| Morgan | 0.0 | 100.0 * † | 44.2 | Scott | 75.9 * † | 24.1 | 52.8 |
| New Madrid | 81.5 | 18.5 | 56.0 | Shannon | 100.0 * † | 0.0 | 58.0 |
| Newton | 48.8 | 51.2 * † | 51.7 | Shelby | 100.0 * † | 0.0 | 66.3 |
| | | | | | | | |
| Nodaway | 54.3 | 45.7 † | 49.4 | Stoddard | 70.3 | 29.7 | 56.5 |
| Oregon | 72.7 * † | 27.3 † | 66.7 | Stone | 24.8 | 75.2 * † | 36.7 |
| Osage | 47.9 | 52.1 † | 44.5 | Sullivan | 54.7 † | 45.3 | 48.9 |
| Ozark | 0.0 | 100.0 | 36.1 | Taney | 44.2 | 55.8 * † | 41.2 |
| Pemiscot | 82.1 † | 17.9 | 55.7 | Texas | 56.8 † | 43.2 | 54.5 |
| | | | | | | | |
| Perry | 0.0 | 100.0 † | 47.1 | Vernon | 54.9 | 45.1 † | 60.9 |
| Pettis | 66.3 | 33.7 * † | 49.0 | Warren | 30.4 | 69.6 † | 23.4 |
| Phelps | 62.5 * † | 37.5 | 49.8 | Washington | 49.3 | 50.7 * † | 41.0 |
| Pike | 61.9 † | 38.1 | 57.9 | Wayne | 56.6 * † | 43.4 | 51.6 |
| Platte | 100.0 * † | 0.0 | 74.0 | Webster | 0.0 | 100.0 * | 49.3 |
| | | | | | | | |
| Polk | 40.7 * | 59.3 * † | 44.3 | | | | |
| Pulaski | 64.9 * † | 35.1 | 57.9 | | | | |
| Putnam | 43.5 | 56.5 † | 37.5 | | | | |
| Ralls | 79.1 † | 20.9 | 68.2 | | | | |
| Randolph | 100.0 † | 0.0 | 67.7 | | | | |

[a] Percentages are of the two-party vote.

| | 1948 General Election | | 1908 | | 1948 General Election | | 1908 |
|---|---|---|---|---|---|---|---|
| District | Per Cent Democratic[a] | Per Cent Republican | Per Cent Democratic | District | Per Cent Democratic[a] | Per Cent Republican | Per Cent Democratic |
| Worth | 58.5† | 41.5 | 51.0 | | | | |
| Wright | 0.0 | 100.0 | 43.8 | | | | |
| St. Louis City I | 49.2 | 50.8† | St. Louis I (3)[b] | St. Louis City X | 68.7 | 31.3† | St. Louis IV (3) |
| | | | 38.4 | | | | 47.9 |
| St. Louis City II | 65.8† | 34.2 | 38.5 | St. Louis City XI | 73.0* | 27.0* | 47.6 |
| | | | 39.0 | | | | 47.4 |
| St. Louis City III | 49.6* | 50.4*† | | St. Louis City XII | 73.6† | 26.4 | |
| St. Louis City IV | 54.5 | 45.5* | St. Louis II (3) | St. Louis City XIII | 59.6 | 40.4† | St. Louis V (2) |
| | | | 45.8 | | | | 46.6 |
| St. Louis City V | 55.6 | 44.4* | 45.8 | St. Louis City XIV | 59.9 | 40.1† | 45.9 |
| | | | 45.4 | | | | |
| St. Louis City VI | 61.1 | 38.9* | | St. Louis City XV | 73.5† | 26.5 | St. Louis VI (2) |
| St. Louis City VII | 65.2 | 34.8† | St. Louis III (3) | St. Louis City XVI | 69.9* | 30.1 | 46.7 |
| | | | 54.3 | | | | 45.0 |
| St. Louis City VIII | 70.9*† | 29.1* | 54.6 | St. Louis City XVII | 67.0* | 33.0 | |
| | | | 54.6 | | | | |
| St. Louis City IX | 78.6*† | 21.4 | | St. Louis City XVIII | 61.1* | 38.9† | |

[a] Percentages are of the two-party vote.

[b] The St. Louis City districts of 1908 and 1948 are not individually comparable. The 1948 districts were single-member districts, whereas in 1908 each district chose the number of members indicated within parentheses. The party percentages in these 1908 multi-membered districts were obtained from a base consisting of the vote of a winner plus the vote of the highest loser of the losing party. Thus, for each district a different base was used for the computation of the percentage to each winner. The reciprocal of that percentage was used as the percentage of the vote to the loser. As may be inferred from the percentages for the several legislators chosen in each 1908 district, the several candidates on each party ticket in each district ran quite closely together.

in each house and between House and Senate groups. What inquiries would be needed for a more complete explanation?

3. The table on pages 194–196 lists the districts of the Missouri House of Representatives and indicates the party percentages of the popular vote by district in the general elections of 1908 and 1948. (An asterisk after a 1948 figure means that the nomination for the party whose percentage is so marked was sought by at least two persons in the 1948 primaries; a dagger indicates that the legislative incumbent was a candidate for renomination in the party's primary. These facts will be needed for a later problem.) Arrange the districts in a frequency table according to the Democratic (or Republican) percentage of the 1908 general election vote; use 10 point intervals. Make a similar table for the 1948 election. Reduce the two tables to comparable form by computing the percentage that each sub-group of a table is of the total number of items in the series it includes. Draw frequency polygons of the two distributions on the same chart and note the differences between the form of the 1908 and 1948 distributions. What developments in American government and politics between the two dates suggest themselves as explanations of the observed differences?

## Chapter 2

1. The table below shows the estimated number of potential voters in presidential election years, 1892–1952, and the numbers

| YEAR | ESTIMATED POTENTIAL VOTE[a] | TOTAL PRESIDENTIAL VOTE | YEAR | ESTIMATED POTENTIAL VOTE[a] | TOTAL PRESIDENTIAL VOTE |
|------|------|------|------|------|------|
| 1892 | 15,860,000 | 12,057,247 | 1924 | 59,287,000 | 29,086,398 |
| 1896 | 17,520,000 | 13,899,857 | 1928 | 64,401,000 | 36,805,450 |
| 1900 | 18,980,000 | 13,964,567 | 1932 | 69,444,000 | 39,731,720 |
| 1904 | 20,613,000 | 13,518,170 | 1936 | 74,416,000 | 45,643,297 |
| 1908 | 22,642,000 | 14,884,265 | 1940 | 79,389,000 | 49,891,051 |
| 1912 | 25,497,000 | 15,034,494 | 1944 | 85,486,000 | 47,969,002 |
| 1916 | 29,938,000 | 18,527,863 | 1948 | 91,431,000 | 48,794,009 |
| 1920 | 54,220,000 | 26,748,224 | 1952 | 95,741,000 | 61,637,951 |

[a] These estimates, made by Laymen Allen, are of the number of citizens meeting the qualifications with respect to age, sex, and citizenship as they existed from election to election.

of votes actually cast. Prepare a graph showing the proportions of the potential electorate actually voting over the period. On the basis of the graph consider the plausibility of the common attribution of the low level of turnout from 1920–1932 almost solely to the Nineteenth Amendment.

2. Identify the five or ten counties in your state that had the widest change in the Democratic (or Republican) percentage of the presidential vote from 1920 to 1952. Determine, by the method used in constructing the inset in Figure 16 on page 54, whether these counties had undergone a gradual and more or less secular realignment. If so, what is the explanation of the realignment? Does your finding suggest further lines of inquiry to seek explanations?

3. Prepare a graph indicating the Democratic or Republican percentage of the two-party vote for governor in your state 1900–1952. Does a cyclical pattern in voter sentiment seem to prevail? Is the State attuned to, or immune from, the tides of national politics?

4. The data accumulated for Exercise 2 of Chapter 1 may be used as an exercise in the computation of the standard deviation. Compute the standard deviation for the party-unity percentages of two groups that were compared in dealing with the earlier problem. Compute also the coefficient of variation for each group. Interpret the meaning of the coefficients as they apply to the particular facts.

### Chapter 3

1. Graph the Democratic or Republican gubernatorial and presidential percentages of the two-party vote at elections in your state from 1900 to the present. Do the two series fluctuate in unison or do they suggest a considerable independence between state and national voting? Do deviations from otherwise uniform relations verify your pre-existing interpretations of particular campaigns or elections? Do they identify elections that would be worthy of special inquiry? What sorts of questions about such elections are suggested by the data?

2. Identify (by reference to Census reports) the half dozen or

so counties in your state that have undergone urbanization in the highest degree since 1900. Compare the trend, if any, in their partisan attachments, using the presidential vote, over the same period with a contrasting handful of counties that have remained completely rural, by the method used in the preparation of Figure 16 on page 54. Do the facts fully fit the simple explanation that probably occurred to you as you read the problem? Does the chart help separate out secular trends from the peculiarities of individual campaigns?

3. Graph the percentage of the popular vote for the candidates of either party for governor in your state from 1920 to date; place on the same chart a graph of the percentage of seats won by the same party in the lower house of the legislature at the elections over the same period. What does the chart tell you about the relationship of voting for governor and for legislative candidates? About the system of representation in the state? About the possibility of a responsible party system? About the relation of trends in national voting to state and local voting? About institutional factors bearing on those relations?

4. Prepare estimates of the number of potential voters in your state in presidential election years, 1920–1952. (Obtain figures for Census years from the Census reports; make appropriate adjustments for the state's sex and citizenship requirements; and interpolate for presidential years not falling in Census years.) Compute the percentage of the estimated electorate actually voting in your state in presidential elections. Compare graphically the state rates with the national rates of participation obtained in Exercise 1 of Chapter 2. What explanation occurs to you for the general relationship between the two series and for exceptional relations, if any, that occur at particular elections?

5. The tabulation on page 200 shows the Republican percentage of the senatorial and gubernatorial vote in Philadelphia, 1918–1938. Graph the two series. Which election appears to have had quite unusual characteristics? Try to discover the odd features of this election by beginning your search with the newspaper and periodical indices.

| YEAR | SENATORIAL REPUBLICAN PERCENTAGE | GUBERNATORIAL REPUBLICAN PERCENTAGE |
|------|------|------|
| 1918 |      | 72.0 |
| 1920 | 76.9 |      |
| 1922 | 81.9 | 79.0 |
| 1926 | 80.6 | 82.3 |
| 1928 | 61.4 |      |
| 1930 | 78.7 | 23.8 |
| 1934 | 50.2 | 51.5 |
| 1938 | 50.9 | 50.8 |

## Chapter 4

1. Prepare a pair of maps appropriately colored or shaded to show the distribution of the counties of your state according to the percentage division of the presidential votes in 1900 and 1920. What marked similarities and dissimilarities occur between the two maps? What does the pattern in the maps suggest about the nature of party loyalties? What demographic or historical factors suggest themselves as broadly associated with the observed pattern?

2. Construct a scatter-diagram with the 1944 Democratic presidential percentage by county in your state as the $X$ variate and the 1948 Democratic county percentage as the $Y$ variate. (The percentages will be found computed in the *Gallup Almanac* for 1952.) What pattern of relationships prevails? Do you identify particular counties in which deviate behavior occurred that might be especially instructive about the nature of the issues of the campaign? (The same exercise could be carried out by the use of the party division of the vote by precinct or ward for a large city; the analysis of such data is often more clear-cut in results than when county data are used.)

3. To obtain a rough measure of the strength of party and of candidate construct a scatter-diagram with the county percentage of the vote for the head of a ticket in your state as the $X$ variate and the county percentage for some other state-wide candidate of the same party at the same election as the $Y$ variate. What does the relationship suggest about the vote-pulling power of particular candidates apart from the general strength of their party? If

particular counties deviate markedly from the general relationship, seek out the explanation.

4. If your state or city is reputed to be governed by a machine, weigh the efficacy of the machine by constructing a scatter-diagram with the percentage of the county or ward vote for one machine candidate for a primary nomination as the $X$ variate and the percentage for another machine candidate at the same primary as the $Y$ variate. Both candidates must, of course, be candidates elected at large in the state or city. (The results will not be very clear unless the candidates for both nominations meet fairly strong opposition at the primary, a factor to be kept in mind in the choice of material for analysis.) What tentative conclusions are suggested about the capacity of the machine to deliver the vote to its slate? About the strength of individual candidates independent of the machine? About areas of machine solidarity and areas of machine weakness? Examination of the newspaper coverage of the campaign will ordinarily be useful in interpreting the relationships established by the diagram.

5. An exercise in the computation of a coefficient of determination and a coefficient of correlation may be performed by the use of any one of the sets of pairs of figures prepared for the four preceding exercises.

### Chapter 5

1. The table of election results for the Missouri House of Representatives given on pages 194–196 provides material for an exercise in cross tabulation. (You may prefer to prepare such a table for the legislature of your own state.) Assume that the problem is to determine whether any relation exists between incumbency and competition for primary nominations. Let it be assumed that two factors are associated with competition for the nomination in a party primary: the candidacy of the incumbent legislator and the continuing strength of the party in the district, which may be measured roughly by its percentage of the vote at the general election. For each party tabulate the primary data for 1948 according to party strength, indicating the proportions of

nominations for which there was competition at each level of party strength. Then cross tabulate according to whether the primary involved an incumbent or did not involve an incumbent, holding constant the factor of party strength. Then determine the proportion of each category of district primaries involving competition at each level of party strength. Does the addition of the tables for the two parties into a single table smooth out some of the irregularities in the relationships suggested by the individual party tables? (All these tabulations may be expedited if the relevant items about each district primary are entered on a card.) Comment on your findings in the light of the problem posed.

## Chapter 6

1. Although the materials in Chapter 6 are in the nature of theory rather than operating guide, they suggest the possibility, if the calendar of elections falls appropriately, of a class exercise in the conduct of a sample survey to estimate the division of the vote in a ward, a small city, or some other manageable electoral unit. The brief treatment in the text will suggest ways and means of sample selection, but for detailed instructions see Mildred Parten, *Surveys, Polls, and Samples: Practical Procedures* (Harper, 1950).

# Index

# INDEX

DATE